Secularism & Science
in the
21st Century

Edited by Ariela Keysar and Barry A. Kosmin

ISSSC

**Institute for the Study of Secularism
in Society and Culture**

Ariela Keysar and Barry A. Kosmin
SECULARISM & SCIENCE IN THE 21ST CENTURY

Copyright © 2008 Ariela Keysar and Barry A. Kosmin

ISBN: 978-0-615-19634-3

Published by

ISSSC

Institute for the Study of Secularism in Society and Culture
Trinity College, Hartford, CT

Cover and book design by Jo Lynn Alcorn

TABLE OF CONTENTS

III. SCIENTIFIC LITERACY AND PUBLIC POLICY

TABLE OF FIGURES

ACKNOWLEDGMENTS

The editors and contributing authors would like to thank
the following individuals for their help and advice
in reviewing and producing this volume:

Jo Lynn Alcorn, Laurie Bonneau, Mark Carnes, Sean Cocco,
Peter Coy, Kay Davidson, Kent Dunlap, Sara Howe,
Jerry Piven, Wayne Proudfoot, Jesse Tisch.

Special thanks to the Posen Foundation
for its continuing support.

Secularism and Science in the 21st Century

Ariela Keysar & Barry A. Kosmin

As this book went to press in early 2008, the Texas Higher Education Coordinating Board was weighing a request by a Bible-based creationist institute to offer online master's degrees in science education. The Institute for Creation Research aims to challenge the standard teachings of evolution and (according to its website) "equip current and future Christian leaders with practical tools to effectively influence their world with the truths of Scripture." Its goal is to staff classrooms with science teachers sympathetic to religious fundamentalism, educators who believe in the Biblical account of the world's creation. This is an open challenge to the normative model of Western science, which is based on the secular principles of free inquiry and empiricism.

Evolution, once again controversial, is only one of the fields of science that has become freshly embroiled in conflict between religious and secular segments of society. Stem cell research, cloning, neuroscience, and paleontology are others. Emotions are strong and the stakes are clearly high. And not for the first time, for in today's battles there are echoes from centuries past. What is surprising is that this "culture war" is fiercest in the United States, the world's first secular state and its oldest and most powerful democracy.

As the eleven essays in the present volume demonstrate, the nature of the conflict over science at the dawn of the third millennium has metamorphosed in important respects. A new divisive factor is the emergence of post-modernist and cultural relativist ideas with a critique that also challenges scientific rationalism. Much has changed since the great battles of the past were fought. This is not the era of Socrates, or of Galileo and the Inquisition, or of the Scopes monkey trial. New thinking is required.

The most important change is that the conflict matters more now than it ever has before given a highly competitive and inter-connected world. Science is a bigger prize today. It is the foundation and *sine qua non* of today's high-tech global economy, which has produced greater material wealth than has ever been seen before. In light of this sweeping achievement, many secular individuals, even those who are not scientifically adept, feel that faith-based challenges to the primacy of scientific reason are deeply threatening to the health and progress of modern society.

Many religiously minded people, for their part, often feel uneasy and even threatened by the growing importance and power of science in society. While scientists claim that their research is value-neutral, religious conservatives assert that scientific advances have made it possible for people to "play God" in such fields as genetic screening and enhancement. What is more, scientists are actively seeking to explain phenomena that were long thought to belong to the realm of religion and the spirit. They are searching for a brain chemistry basis for altruism, for example, and evolutionary origins for belief in a higher being and the supernatural.

Secularism and Science in the 21st Century grew out of work done under the auspices of the Institute for the Study of Secularism in Society and Culture (ISSSC) of Trinity College in Hartford, Conn. ISSSC is a non-partisan and multi-disciplinary institute established in 2005 to advance understanding of the role of secular values and the process of secularization in contemporary society and culture. In May 2007, ISSSC organized a workshop and a roundtable discussion on "Science Education and Secular Values." Leading scientists from various universities in the U.S. contemplated topical issues such as the competing influences of secularism and religion on science education as well as scientific literacy in a postmodern world. Simultaneously, during the academic year 2006-07 ISSSC faculty fellows designed new undergraduate courses, as part of the ISSSC curriculum development program, under the theme: "The Secular Tradition and Foundations of the Natural Sciences." And in the winter of 2006-07 ISSSC sponsored a unique essay contest among Connecticut high school students asking their opinions of why most American students are not interested in science education.

This book has three parts. The first contains four essays with differing approaches to dealing with the ongoing conflict over evolution vs. creation. The second part offers strategies for the pedagogical challenges of teaching science. The book concludes with a public policy concern, scientific literacy, an issue which has major political and economic consequences for society and culture.

Jon D. Miller and Robert Pennock, in addressing the conflict over evolution vs. creation, say the "center must hold" in order to sustain the democratic system of government. Their political strategy is a call for centrists to resist the attempts of what they call "the religious extreme to undermine sound science education."

Daniel G. Blackburn maintains that creationism represents the most public manifestation of a broad-based and well-financed effort to replace secular society with a theocratic state. For creationism to be true, he claims, most of what was learned in natural sciences, and much of what was learned in humanities and social sciences, would have to be untrue. Thus it is, he says, "an assault on knowledge and on rationality."

Austin Dacey finds merit in the arguments of one of the most militant atheists, Richard Dawkins. He identifies what he calls "the Dawkins effect," which by highlighting the conflict between science and religion actually raises awareness of messages of science-religion harmony and encourages the moderate middle to try to solve the conflict.

Frank L. Pasquale observes that wholesale conflict between advocates of "religion" and "science" is more intense in the United States than elsewhere. It is largely absent, for example, in Asia. He bemoans the tendency for each side to take a monolithic and unyielding approach, and suggests that many forms of religiosity are compatible with science.

In teaching science, one of the challenges is if, and how, to present both sides—evolution and creationism. William Cobern criticizes "philosophical secularism," which is difficult for religious students to accept, and advocates instead "methodological secularism" as a tool to defuse the controversy over science education in public schools. He calls for teaching science, not scientism. Cobern suggests that students be allowed to explore their own ideas even though he realizes that this approach might open the classroom door to creationism, and might be counter to standard science.

David E. Henderson reflects on his experience developing college science courses and implementing methodological secularism in the classroom. His detailed examples of a new pedagogy, *Reacting to the Past*, demonstrate how the rules for teaching science proposed by Cobern could be put into practice in college courses.

Benjamin Beit-Hallahmi reviews the historical struggles and culture wars to secularize the American education systems, from the ivory tower of academia to the public schools. He discusses why evolution became the contested issue between what he labels as "warm religion" and "cold science."

Juan Antonio Aguilera Mochón contributes an international perspective to the volume by exploring the teaching of science and religion in Catholic Spain, arguing strongly against mixing the two domains. His purist approach is to keep the doors firmly closed to accommodating unscientific teaching in public education.

Jeffrey Burkhardt challenges the Science Establishment, arguing that its members have a "vested interest in Scientific Literacy." He argues that one ought to respect the right of others to believe in creationism, astrology, and Scientology, even if these are all (scientifically) wrong.

In debating the role of scientific literacy, Barry A. Kosmin and Juhem Navarro-Rivera assert the close relationship between secularism and democracy particularly regarding crucial decisions related to the common good. Kosmin and Navarro-Rivera claim that only well-informed citizens can fulfill their responsibilities in a democratic society when the public is asked as voters or jurors to weigh in on issues such as bio-medical treatments, DNA evidence, the environment, and energy consumption. In this they disagree with Burkhardt, who cites an imaginary "Ralph the barber" who is happily—and successfully— ignorant of science. Burkhardt poses a philosophical question: will having more knowledgeable people make America a better place to live? This is a critical dilemma. In an economically developed U.S. there is a division of labor and division of skill of expertise and indeed many "Ralphs" can live a productive life.

In addition to their point about "holding the center," Miller and Pennock claim that the poor performance of U.S. high schools in teaching science and mathematics contributes to American adults' minimal understanding of biological education. Americans, they claim, are unprepared to progress in scientific research and so maintain the nation's technological advantage into the future.

Ariela Keysar and Frank L. Pasquale focus on individuals. They make use of the rare opportunity to hear directly from young people, potentially the next generation of scientists, expressing their ideas about their own generation's lack of interest in science education. Some of the critical observations that the high school students make shed light on the perceptions of contemporary young people regarding science and science education. The students' blunt criticism directed towards their own generation as well as the educational system ought to be seriously reviewed. For those who are interested in brainstorming some alternatives or options for the U.S. to compete internationally in science education, the students' opinions and suggestions are enlightening.

The current contest between secular and religious values raises a number of questions. How can science education serve a population of students with diverse values, concerns and life experiences? What educational and pedagogical tools are needed to introduce such a model to the classroom in the 21st century? What should research scientists and educators do to assume a leadership role in debates about the values of science, and the value of science to the well-being of individuals and society?

The reader will find liberal religious responses and a range of "soft" and "hard" secular responses presented in this volume, and the voices and insights of both Americans and non-Americans, trying to reconcile to various degrees faith and reason. While not necessarily agreeing with each other, the scholars offer useful intellectual frameworks as well as advice and practical solutions in all three of the areas covered by this book: ideology, pedagogy, and public policy. We hope that the reader finds each essay a provocative and positive contribution to important on-going debates, and that the whole is greater than the sum of the parts.

The Evolution-Creation Conflict

1. Science Education and Religion in America in the 21st Century: Holding the Center

Jon D. Miller & Robert T. Pennock

For most of the 19th and 20th centuries, there has been an uneasy truce between science and religion in the United States. During the 60 years since the end of the Second World War, the United States has been viewed as the most scientific nation on the planet. American universities and laboratories have developed an extraordinary array of technologies, and are responsible for a substantial portion of our modern scientific understanding of nature. More Americans have been early adopters of new technologies—from automobiles and airplanes to antibiotics and new medical technologies—than adults in any other country. Nine out of ten Americans think that science and technology have made their lives "healthier, easier, and more comfortable." And yet, on particular issues such as evolution and stem cell research, there has been active political resistance to scientific advancement from at least some religious quarters. Such religious opposition has led to a low-level but ongoing struggle over the content of science education.

Studies of public attitudes toward science and technology reveal that many Americans feel conflicted about science and religion. The baseline measurement in this field is a 1957 study conducted by the University of Michigan just two months before the launch of Sputnik I. It was a comprehensive study of public understanding of science and technology and attitudes toward selected policy areas. Miller[1] and others have repeated these questions over the last 50 years. The results show that a substantial majority of Americans think that science and technology have improved the quality of their lives and are increasing opportunities for the next generation (see *Figure 1-1*). However, the answer to another question reveals the simultaneous presence of a continuing level of religious discomfort with science. The survey item asks respondents to strongly agree, agree, disagree, or strongly disagree with the statement: "We

Figure 1-1
Attitudes Toward Science and Technology, 1957-2005[26]

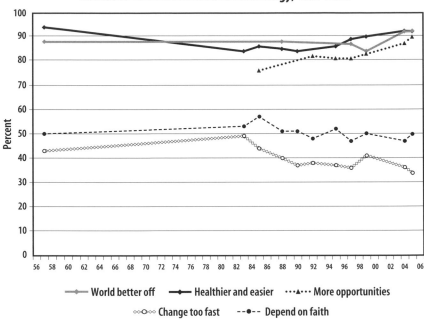

——◆—— World better off   ——◆—— Healthier and easier   ···▲··· More opportunities

∞∞○∞∞ Change too fast   --●-- Depend on faith

depend too much on science and not enough on faith." Half of American adults agreed with that statement in 1957 and in 2005. Although that percentage has varied over the last five decades, it is clear that this issue remains a point of concern for many adults.

These two sets of views illustrate the continuing tension between science and religion in the United States. When American adults are asked to balance these two views, the results show that they tend to favor the promise of science and technology over their reservations. Asked the direct question "Is the world better off or worse off because of science?"—88% of adults thought that the world was better off because of science in 1957, on the eve of Sputnik, and 92% expressed the same view in 2005. These results might suggest that the current controversies over evolution and stem cell research reflect the concerns of only a small proportion of American adults and that the post-war American embrace of science and technology is unchallenged. A more careful analysis, however, reveals that while there is strong support for science and technology, there are strongly held religious views that conflict with modern science. Moreover, these latter views have become amplified in recent decades as Christian fundamentalists established themselves as a powerful force in American politics, seeking to insert their views into science classes and establish them as the norm. There is also a sizable group of people in the middle whose general support for science may be vulnerable in particular areas. The question for American science education in the 21st century is whether the center will hold in the face of pressure from religious conservatives.

This chapter examines evidence that may help answer this question. A more fine-grained analysis of the data indicates that, despite the high and in some cases increasing level of pro-science attitudes, there remains a substantial number of Americans who have reservations about science—reservations that could be exploited—and it would be unwise to be complacent about the strength of support for sound science education. The religious right has attempted to erode this support by using evolution as a wedge issue, though there are some recent indications that this tactic is losing its effectiveness. Understanding the nature of the threat posed by the religious right may help scientists and educators find ways to further blunt the creationist wedge and improve public understanding of science in the process. We conclude this chapter by making a few recommendations about things that might be done.

Public Acceptance of Science in the United States

Social scientists, like our colleagues in the life sciences and the physical sciences, must always be aware of our instrumentation and its potential impact on our measurements. In this case, a careful analysis of the results shown above suggests that there is less certainty and greater ambivalence toward these views than a simple agree-disagree dichotomy would suggest. Over similar periods of time, some of these questions have been asked with different sets of response categories; and so a comparison of these sets of data provides some important insights into the firmness of public attitudes toward science and technology.

An examination of the full set of responses—strongly agree, agree, disagree, strongly disagree, or not sure—to the statement "science and technology have made our lives healthier, easier, and more comfortable" shows a slightly different picture of public attitudes over the last 20 years (see *Figure 1-2*). Although approximately two-thirds of adults agreed with this statement during the last 20 years, these data indicate that the proportion of adults who "strongly agree" with this statement grew from 19% in 1985 to 29% in 2005. For this specific statement, the opposition has diminished in both size and intensity during the last 20 years. On balance, these data show that although there is broad public acceptance of the idea that science and technology have improved the quality of our lives, a majority of adults are only moderately committed to this proposition.

A 2003 national study of American adults asked essentially the same question, with a slight difference: it asked respondents to express their degree of agreement on a zero-to-10 scale, with zero meaning that they disagree completely and 10 meaning that they agree completely. This metric is widely used in European surveys, and the 2003 study was the U.S. component of a 10-country study that included nine European countries. When viewed on this metric, it is clear that there are a variety of levels of agreement with the idea that science and technology have made out lives healthier, easier, and more comfortable. A total of 44% of American adults agreed with this statement at the level of 8, 9, or 10, which is slightly higher than the 29% who were willing to say "strongly agree" (see *Figure 1-3*).

From these three views of the same attitude, it appears that there is a substantial plurality of American adults who believe that science and technology make their lives healthier, easier, and more comfortable, and that only about 6% of adults in the U.S. disagree strongly with this idea.

On the other side of the issue, it is useful to look at how people respond to another statement: "We depend too much on science and not enough on faith." A more detailed examination of the responses suggests that although the proportion of strongly held views on this statement has increased over the last 20 years, a substantial majority of Americans holds much more moderate attitudes on this issue. Throughout the 20-year period from 1985 to 2005, 37% of American adults "disagreed" with the statement, but not strongly. Similarly, the proportion of adults who "agreed" with the statement declined from 49% in 1985 to 37% in 2005, with most of this loss appearing as "strongly agree" in 2005 (see *Figure 1-4*). It is important to note that American adults have been almost equally divided over this issue throughout the last 20 years, and that the proportion of adults who indicate that they "don't know" has decreased slightly during this period.

The same question about science and faith was asked in the 2003 U.S. study using a zero-to-10 response metric. The responses show that about 10% of American adults completely agree with the statement and 10% completely disagree (see *Figure 1-5*). If a response of 8, 9, or 10 denotes a high level of agreement with the statement, 29% of American adults have a high level of agreement that we depend too much on science and not enough on faith, compared to 21% with a comparable level of disagreement. The remaining 50% of American adults hold a mixed or uncertain attitude about the conflict between scientific and religious ideas.

From this analysis of two basic attitudes toward science and technology, it appears that there is a high level of agreement that science and technology have improved the quality of our lives, making our lives healthier, easier, and more

Figure 1-2

Science and Technology Make Our Lives Healthier, Easier, and More Comfortable[27]

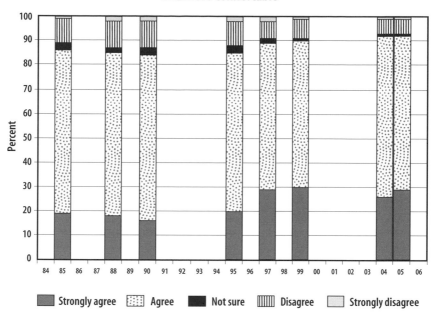

Figure 1-3

Science and Technology Make Our Lives Healthier, Easier, and More Comfortable, 2003[28]

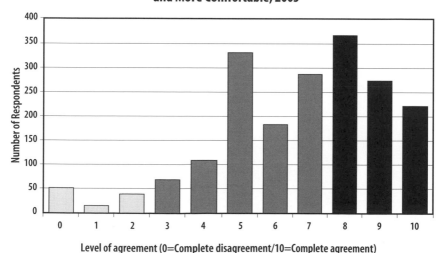

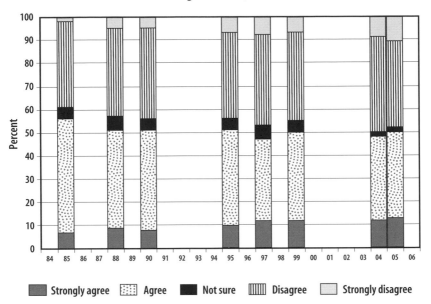

Figure 1-4

Agreement with the Statement that We Depend Too Much on Science and Not Enough on Faith, 1985-2005[29]

■ Strongly agree　▦ Agree　■ Not sure　▥ Disagree　□ Strongly disagree

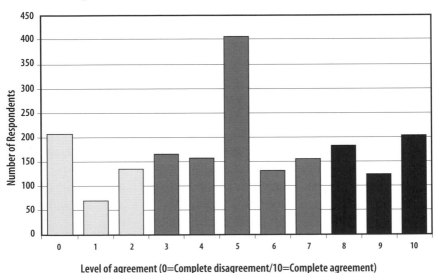

Figure 1-5

Level of Agreement with Science and Faith Statement on 0-10 Metric, 2003[30]

Level of agreement (0=Complete disagreement/10=Complete agreement)

comfortable. There is equally strong agreement that science and technology will provide new opportunities for the next generation of Americans. At the same time, a substantial proportion of American adults holds some reservations about the relative influence of faith and science. A dichotomous treatment of responses to the science and faith issue would indicate that roughly half of American adults are troubled by this conflict, but an examination of the same attitude using other metrics suggests that about 30% of American adults have significant reservations on this issue. This is still a substantial number of adults—approximately 64 million adults.

Moreover, these numbers do not tell the whole story. An important factor to keep in mind is that many leaders of this segment of the population see themselves as fighting a "culture war" against what they believe to be the corrupting influence of the modern scientific worldview. They believe that "modernist" and "materialist" science undermines faith; and they want to reinvent science in a form that is not only consistent with, but also supports, their theistic conviction that man is created in God's image. Though in the past this segment of Christian fundamentalists responded by withdrawing from the world, in recent decades their leaders have succeeded in awakening them as a political force. With missionary energy, they have sought to bring about a "renewal" of what they take to be the Christian foundation of the country. Through a combination of political alliances and promotion of strategic wedge issues, they have sought to convert (or at least co-opt) those in the soft middle to their side. One cannot understand the ongoing battle over science and science education in the United States unless one appreciates the views and goals of this large group on the religious extreme.

Religious Fundamentalism in America

At the beginning of the 21st century, the percentage of American adults who held fundamentalist religious beliefs was higher than in any country in Europe or the European Union collectively. The roots of Protestant fundamentalism in the United States are long and deep, traceable in some cases to the earliest settlers in North America. Europeans and Americans have quite different religious histories and experiences, and although a full discussion of those differences is beyond the scope of this analysis, there are some aspects of the growth of religious fundamentalism in the United States that are, indeed, relevant to this analysis.

Fundamentalism in the United States has been built on two central premises. First, fundamentalists insist that the Bible is the word of God and that it must be accepted literally. They strongly reject the idea that the Bible is metaphorical or that it is one of several important religious books. Fundamentalist Christians are one-book religionists in almost exactly the same sense as fundamentalist Muslims, except that they disagree about which book holds the word of God.

Second, fundamentalist Christians believe in a personal God who knows their name, hears their prayers, keeps score, has the power to intervene in their daily lives, and ultimately provides rewards or punishments in a future life. For many adults who hold these fundamentalist beliefs, it is important to see human beings as the direct creation of God—as a whole person. The story of Adam and Eve is taken literally. Any concept of evolution that traces the development of current humans from microbial life is seen as inherently wrong.

Data from recent national surveys in the United States provide some estimates of the proportion of American adults who currently hold these fundamentalist views. In a national study of adults in 2005, each respondent was asked if he or she "strongly agreed, agreed, disagreed, strongly disagreed, or were unsure" about each of the following statements:

> The Bible is the actual word of God and is to be taken literally.

> There is a personal God who hears the prayers of individual men and women.

> Human beings were created by God as whole persons and did not evolve from earlier forms of life.

A total of 43% of American adults agreed or strongly agreed with all three statements[2] (see *Figure 1-6*). An additional 20% of adults agreed with two of the three statements. Only 18% of adults disagreed or strongly disagreed with all three statements. Miller, Scott & Okamoto[3] found that American adults ranked 33rd out of 34 countries in their acceptance of biological evolution. We do not yet have comparable data on public understanding of the nature of empirical science and of its evidence-based methods, but probably these would be equally dismal.

The co-existence of this level of fundamentalism with a strong and growing scientific community fuels a good deal of the current controversy over evolution, stem cell research, and other issues about the beginning of life and the end of life. Rather than being a narrow set of problematic issues, these disputes symbolize a new era of public policy dispute over the control and uses of science and technology. It is noteworthy that these disputes involve both empirical and ethical issues. Although philosophers point out that questions about facts and values are very different, many fundamentalists see the proper moral order as built into the very structure of nature, namely by virtue of God's creation of the world, especially the biological world, with specific purposes in mind.[4] To

Figure 1-6
Selected Religious Attitudes, 2005[35]

	Agree	Strongly Agree	Not Sure	Disagree	Strongly Disagree
The Bible is the actual word of God and is to be taken literally.	27%	27%	2%	27%	17%
There is a personal God who hears the prayers of individual men and women.	38%	33%	4%	15%	10%
Human beings were created by God as whole persons and did not evolve from earlier forms of life.	37%	25%	2%	20%	16%
Number of agreements or strong agreements to the preceding statements:				0	18%
				1	19%
				2	20%
				3	43%
N = 1,484					

give just one example, the "Wedge" document, a leaked internal manifesto from the key ID organization, the Discovery Institute, speaks of "[t]he proposition that human beings are created in the image of God" and says that "modern science" denied the objective moral standards that come from this theistic understanding of nature by putting forward a view of the universe as "ruled by purely impersonal forces." It blames modern science for everything from moral relativism to modern approaches to product liability and welfare, and offers Intelligent Design (ID) as a "wedge" that will break apart materialist science and "replace it with a science consonant with Christian and theistic convictions."[5] It is important to recognize that this is not just an attack on biology, but on science itself. However we will here focus on just the idea of being created in the image of God as a key element of the fundamentalist worldview that makes evolution such an important issue for them. The antipathy that so many Americans feel toward the idea of being related to animals is part of the reason that the religious right has used evolution as a political wedge issue.

Americans' Attitudes Toward Evolution

Before examining the current situation, it is worth noting that mainstream Christianity does not have a problem with evolution and that, historically, even evangelical and fundamentalist Christians were more accepting than they are now. People often forget that evangelical Christian scientists were among the early defenders of evolution following the publication of Darwin's *The Origin of the Species* in 1859.[6] The series of religious tracts called *The Fundamentals*, out of which American fundamentalism grew, saw no necessary conflict between evolution and Genesis. Even at the time of the Scopes trial, the standard fundamentalist interpretation of Genesis (as seen in the Scofield Reference Bible) allowed that the Earth could be ancient. But the simplifying tenets of fundamentalism that lead to its broad popularity also led it naturally away from organized theological training and over time any theological sophistication about Biblical interpretation that had initially kept it open to scientific findings was progressively lost. Today, fundamentalists who insist on the infallibility of the Bible, the Koran, or any other single religious text typically reject both the concept and the science of evolution.[7] The concept of the evolution of humans from earlier forms of life has provoked the ire of conservative religious leaders and generated significant public resistance in the United States. Current efforts to insert ID into school science curricula constitute an attempt to unite young-earth and old-earth creationists around the core idea of the transcendent design of humans and the rest of the biological world, and to temporarily set aside the question of the age of the Earth and the co-existence of humans and dinosaurs.[8]

The current controversy over evolution illustrates the nature of the ongoing conflict. A majority of American adults indicate that they believe humans were created as whole persons directly by God and that humans are uniquely different from other animals and from plants. This provides an opening that creationists try to exploit to bring people in the middle to their side.

Over the last two decades, there have been a number of measurements of the public acceptance of the concept of evolution, long a target of religious fundamentalists in the United States. Beginning in 1985, national samples of American adults[9] have been asked whether the statement "Human beings, as we know them, developed from earlier species of animals" is true or false, or whether the respondent is not sure or does not know. Over the last 20 years, the percentage of adults accepting the idea of evolution has declined from 45% to 40% and the percentage of adults rejecting evolution declined from 48% to 39% (see *Figure 1-7*). The percentage of adults who were not sure about evolution increased from 7% in 1985 to 21% in 2005. After 20 years of public debate, the public appears to be divided evenly in terms of accepting or rejecting evolution, with about one in five adults still undecided or unaware of the issue. This pattern is consistent with a number of sporadic national newspaper surveys reported in recent years.[10] It is this larger soft middle group—the swing vote—that will decide what happens in the battle over science education. And a more

Figure 1-7
Acceptance or Rejection of Evolution, 1985-2005[31]

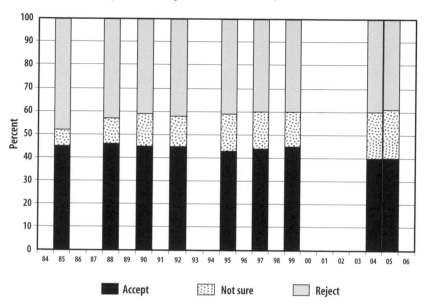

fine-grained analysis of the survey data suggests that support for evolution is weaker than even these numbers indicate.

As noted in regard to general attitudes toward science and technology, the dichotomous true-false question format used in most of the surveys in the United States and other countries concerning the acceptance or rejection of evolution tends to exaggerate the strength of both positions. In 1993 and 2003, national samples of American adults were asked about the same statement—human beings developed from earlier species of animals—but were offered the choice of saying that the statement was "definitely true, probably true, probably false, definitely false," or that they did not know or were uncertain. The results show that approximately a third of American adults firmly reject evolution and that only 14% of adults think that evolution is "definitely true" (see *Figure 1-8*). Treating the probably true, probably false, and not sure categories as varying degrees of uncertainty, approximately 55% of American adults have held a tentative view about evolution for the last decade.

This pattern of acceptance, rejection, and uncertainty among American adults is significantly different from Europe and Japan. Looking at the true-false question, an analysis found that significantly more adults in Japan and 31 European countries accepted the concept of evolution than American adults

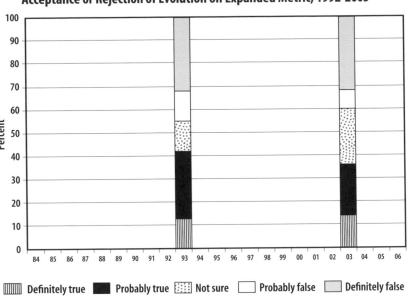

Figure 1-8

Acceptance or Rejection of Evolution on Expanded Metric, 1992-2003[32]

Definitely true   Probably true   Not sure   Probably false   Definitely false

(see *Figure 1-9*). Only Turkish adults were less likely to accept the concept of evolution than American adults. Eighty percent or more of adults in Iceland, Denmark, Sweden, and France accepted the concept of evolution, as did 78% of Japanese adults. Two-thirds of adults in the United Kingdom, Norway, Belgium, Spain, Germany, Italy, the Netherlands, Hungary, Luxembourg, Ireland, Slovenia, Finland, and the Czech Republic accepted evolution, and the proportion of adults in these European countries that rejected evolution rarely reached 25%. In contrast, approximately 40% of American adults refuse to accept the idea of evolution.[11]

Using data from 10 countries collected in 2002 and 2003 with the expanded response set, American adults were significantly less likely to think that evolution is definitely or probably true than adults in nine European countries (see *Figure 1-10*). Following the pattern noted in the other data sets, 32% of American adults indicated that evolution was "absolutely false" compared to 7% of adults in Britain, Denmark, and France. Only 14% of American adults thought that evolution was "absolutely true," compared to 53% of Danish adults and 39% of French adults who saw evolution as absolutely true.[12]

The results of a 2005 U.S. study suggest that substantial numbers of American adults are more confused than ideological with regard to 20th and

Figure 1-9
Acceptance or Rejection of Evolution in 34 Countries, 2005[33]

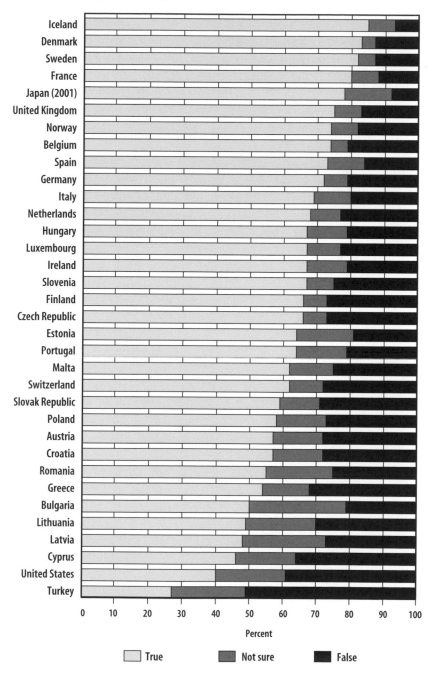

Figure 1-10

Acceptance or Rejection of Evolution in 10 Countries, 2002, 2003[34]

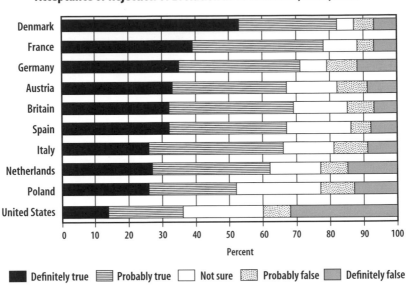

21st century biology. When presented with a description of natural selection that omits the word evolution, 78% of adults agree with or accept a description of the evolution of plants and animals (see *Figure 1-11*). But 62% of adults in the same study believe that God created humans as whole persons without any evolutionary development. It appears that many of these adults have adopted a human exceptionalism perspective—plants and animals developed through a process of natural selection but that humans were exempted from that process and created directly.

Elements of this human exceptionalism perspective can be seen in the way that many adults try to integrate modern genetics into their understanding of life. For example, only a third of American adults agree that more than half of human genes are identical to those of mice and only 38% of adults recognize that humans have more than half of their genes in common with chimpanzees. The idea that 90% of our genes are identical to genes found in mice and chimpanzees undoubtedly challenges the idea of human exclusiveness. In other studies, we have found that fewer than half of American adults can provide a minimal definition of DNA, thus it is not surprising that nearly half of the respondents in the 2005 study were not sure about the number of human genes that overlap with mice or chimpanzees.[13]

Viewed in the context of these other beliefs, it appears that substantial

Figure 1-11
Acceptance or Rejection of Selected Scientific Constructs, 2005[36]

	True	Not sure	False
Over periods of millions of years, some species of plants and animals adjust and survive while other species die and become extinct. (T)	78%	16%	6%
More than half of human genes are identical to those of mice. (T)	32%	47%	21%
Human beings have somewhat less than half of the DNA in common with chimpanzees. (F)	15%	48%	38%
The earliest humans lived at the same time as the dinosaurs. (F)	28%	22%	51%
Human beings were created by God as whole persons and did not evolve from earlier forms of life. (F)	62%	2%	36%
Human beings, as we know them today, developed from earlier species of animals. (T)	40%	21%	39%
N = 1,484			

numbers of American adults are confused about the content and meaning of modern biology. Although there is undoubtedly a religious predisposition toward seeing humans as the direct product of divine creation, many religions and religious groups have been willing to see the biblical story of the Garden of Eden as metaphorical and to accept modern biology as a means to an end. For instance, the Roman Catholic Church has accepted evolution as a scientific fact and interpreted it as a means to human creation. This traditional Catholic view accounts in large part for the substantial differences observed earlier between the United States and major European nations.

The Struggle over Science Education

This continuing dispute over evolution has influenced the teaching of the life sciences in American secondary schools. From the trial of John Scopes in 1925 for teaching evolution in his public school classroom to the present efforts to change state science curriculum standards in Kansas and Ohio, religious fundamentalists have fought the teaching of modern biology.

One of the effects of the politicization of evolution for partisan purposes has been increased pressure on local teachers to either omit any reference to evolution or to include a Creationist alternative. The Creationist movement as we know it today arose as a response to the 1968 Supreme Court case that overturned laws that had banned the teaching of evolution.[14] Initially, fundamentalists attempted to reinsert their religious view into the schools under the term "creation science." Although they did this without explicitly mentioning God or the Bible, the Supreme Court in 1987 ruled that Creation science was not science but disguised religion. Undaunted, Creationists sharpened and relabeled their view "intelligent design" and tried again, though in 2005 the courts found that ID, too, was simply disguised sectarian religion.[15] Their latest approach is to avoid mentioning either Creation science or Intelligent Design by name, but to insert them indirectly by calling for laws and policies that require students to learn "arguments for and against" evolution and including Creationist writings such as those by Michael Behe, William Dembski, Jonathan Wells, and others as examples of critical resources. Fundamentalists continue to pressure local school boards, state school boards, and individual teachers. The cumulative effect has been chilling. Many teachers, administrators, school board members, and textbook publishers seek to avoid public confrontations by avoiding the subject.

Nor is biology the only target. Fundamentalists have also attacked geology and physics, working to remove references in the curriculum to the geological time scale, the age of the earth and the Big Bang, for instance. And recent bills have called for students to question not just the evidence for evolution, but also global warming, another scientific topic that has become politicized.

The results from the Second International Mathematics and Science Study (SIMSS) and the Third International Mathematics and Science Study (TIMSS) are compelling and disappointing. The poor performance of American students is not measurement error; it reflects real problems in secondary education in the United States. Although there are numerous factors involved in the failure of American science education at the pre-collegiate level, the avoidance of fundamentalist attacks is one important contributor to the current outcome.

Even more worrisome than fundamentalists' attacks upon specific scientific findings in biology, geology, physics, and so on, is their more general attack on the very foundations of scientific reasoning. In their quest for a science consonant with Christian and theistic convictions, as the ID Wedge document described it, they aim to overturn the ground rules of science so as to recognize explanations that appeal to supernatural beings and powers.[16] In calling for unscientific "alternative theories" to be taught on a par with well-established scientific findings, they are unfairly promoting views that have not earned their place by surviving the rigors of scientific testing. By requiring students to learn so-called "arguments for and against" scientific theories, they are undermining the evidence-based reasoning that stands behind established science and replacing it with a relativism of empirical knowledge that would destroy the empirical methods that make science work.

Given the poor performance of U.S. high schools in teaching science and mathematics, the current educational system is creating a steady flow of American adults who will have a minimal understanding of biological science and who will be unprepared to maintain the level of research progress that has given the nation its scientific and technological advantage.

The Emergence of Ideological Politics in the United States

This problem becomes more serious in the context of an increasingly ideological political system in the United States. Until recent decades, science policy in the United States has been largely bipartisan in nature. Both major political parties have endorsed Vannevar Bush's idea of a contract between science and society[17] and have jointly supported the creation and growth of major scientific institutions such as the National Institutes of Health, the National Science Foundation, and a network of national laboratories. The war on cancer was a war that both parties endorsed and supported.

The evidence indicates that the traditional non-partisan treatment of science policy issues has ended.[18] Although a substantial majority of Americans continue to believe that science and technology will make their lives healthier, easier, and more comfortable, a set of life science issues—evolution, stem cell research, genetic modification, abortion, euthanasia—have become a part of partisan politics. The current emphasis on biomedical research and agricultural biotechnology in the United States and throughout the modern world will bring an increasing number of science-related issues into public policy discussions.

The decision to politicize issues such as evolution and stem cell research was not inevitable. Indeed, no political party in Europe[19] or Japan or any other major industrial country has attempted to politicize these issues. There have been previous attempts to politicize evolution in the United States, a famous example being the Scopes trial in 1925. In the second half of the 20th century, however, conservative Republicans identified evolution as an effective wedge issue and have used the rejection of evolution as a litmus test for political conservatism for several decades. In the 1990s, the state Republican platforms in Alaska, Iowa, Kansas, Oklahoma, Oregon, Missouri, and Texas included explicit demands for the teaching of Creation science. John C. Danforth, a former Republican Senator from Missouri and an Episcopalian minister, recently wrote in a *New York Times* Op-Ed piece:

By a series of recent initiatives, Republicans have transformed our party into the political arm of conservative Christians. The elements of this transformation have included advocacy of a constitutional amendment to ban gay marriage, opposition to stem cell research involving both frozen embryos and human cells in petri dishes, and the extraordinary effort to keep Terri Schiavo hooked up to a feeding tube.[...]

I do not fault religious people for political action. Since Moses confronted the pharaoh, faithful people have heard God's call to political involvement. Nor has political action been unique to conservative Christians. Religious liberals have been politically active in support of gay rights and against nuclear weapons and the death penalty. In America, everyone has the right to try to influence political issues, regardless of his religious motivations.

The problem is not with people or churches that are politically active. It is with a party that has gone so far in adopting a sectarian agenda that it has become the political extension of a religious movement.[20]

In fairness, it is important to recognize that not all Republicans are fundamentalists and not all fundamentalists are Republicans, but there is a reasonably high correlation. Looking at data from the 2005 Science News Study,[21] 44% of religious fundamentalists describe themselves as Republicans and 25% say that they are political independents. As one might expect in the current political environment in the United States, 64% of religious fundamentalists classified themselves as Republicans in the "red" states, compared to 56% in the "battleground states" and 48% in the "blue states."

It is also important to look at the distribution of fundamentalists within each of the major political parties. In both parties, it is the primary elections that determine the candidates that are on the ballot for the November elections. Political scientists and election specialists know that voters in most Republican primaries are more conservative than the average adult who identifies with the Republican Party and that, similarly, voters in Democratic primaries are more liberal than the average Democratic voter. The point that John Danforth makes is that fundamentalist Christians now constitute a majority (or near majority) in many Republican states, and therefore in Republican primaries in those states. An analysis of data from a national study in 2004 shows that 65% of Republicans in "red" states were religiously conservative or fundamentalist, and 61% of Republicans in "battleground states" were religiously conservative or fundamentalist. Conversely, 68% of Democrats in "blue states" and 62% of

Democrats in "battleground states" held moderate or liberal religious views.

As a result of several decades of gradual political realignment in the United States, two ideologically distinct political parties now exist, and science issues have become a part of both parties' platforms. Republicans often support the teaching of Creationism and oppose stem cell research, and Democrats take the opposite positions. As mentioned, the religious right has, with some success, used evolution as a political wedge issue, although there are some recent signs that the strategy may be backfiring. The recent defeat of Intelligent Design in court[22] was so resounding that even leaders of the Intelligent Design movement have ceased mentioning the term, as they try to regroup and rethink their political strategy. Just as significantly, recent school board, gubernatorial, and Senate elections resulted in the defeat of candidates who were known for their anti-evolutionism. Conservative political opinion-makers, from Charles Krauthammer to the *National Review*'s John Derbyshire, have begun publicly questioning the value of anti-evolutionism to conservatism. George Will, for instance, wrote that the school board members who favored ID were "the kind of conservatives who make conservatism repulsive to temperate people."[23] In a recent debate the Republican candidates were asked about their stand on evolution. The three who said they doubted evolution all tried to backpedal in subsequent days, as their answers were perceived as extremist. Hopefully, this trend will continue. Otherwise, the currently polarized ideological character of American politics will create new problems and challenges for the scientific community generally, but especially for science educators at the pre-collegiate level.

Science Education in the 21st Century

Scientists and science educators in the United States face a strange dilemma. At the beginning of the 21st century, American science and technology are widely respected throughout the world. The American hegemony in various fields in the immediate post-war decades is largely gone, but the quality of American research universities and the creativity of American scientists and engineers are admired throughout the world. The continuing pressure from students throughout the world to gain admission to American universities—and especially American graduate and professional schools—is evidence of continuing achievement and success in many fields. At the same time, a revitalized religious fundamentalism is producing a serious political challenge to the success of the scientific enterprise. When the Bush administration's religiously based policy on stem cell research seriously disadvantaged American scientists, a combination of private foundations and state governments had to step forward to sustain an essential core of high-quality stem cell work. Every time another Creationist attack on science makes headlines around the world, such as happened with high-profile cases in Kansas, Ohio and Pennsylvania, the reputation of American science education is sullied.

In this environment, science educators face a dual challenge. On the one hand, colleges and universities are expected to produce future generations of scientists and engineers who will be capable of harnessing emerging science and thus be responsible for improving people's quality of life and improving the economic competitiveness of each nation. The logic of this task indicates the need to identify talented students early and provide them with a quality education through the undergraduate and graduate years, plus a research or professional career. This is often translated into a "best and brightest" strategy.

At the same time, science educators must take substantial responsibility for the education of future citizens. Traditionally, the education of citizens was thought to be the responsibility of general education and perhaps a high school civics teacher. Citizenship meant knowing how government works. But at the beginning of the 21st century, it is clear that the responsibility for preparing future generations of citizens belongs to all educators, including science educators, mathematics educators, social science educators, and teachers of art, letters, and the humanities. An adult who does not understand some basic scientific constructs—the nature of matter and life, the role of DNA, and so on—will have a difficult time understanding public policy issues like global warming. Those who do not know the history of humans on this planet may repeat the mistakes of earlier generations. And those who do not understand evolutionary science may not appreciate either the significance of their doctor's instruction to complete all the prescribed doses of antibiotics, nor evolution's important role in agriculture, industry, and environmental management.

At the secondary level, it is essential to abandon the present smorgasbord approach to science and mathematics education and to take seriously the challenge of making every high school graduate scientifically literate. Through a complex tracking system, American high schools provide a minimally credible science education to about a third of students who find their way into an "honors" science course. Students outside the honors track get primarily 19th-century physics and a little pond biology. What little is taught about the nature of scientific inquiry is superficial at best. For reasons of self-preservation, too many high school science teachers try to teach biology with a minimal exposure to the concepts of natural selection and evolutionary biology. This needs to change. Evolution should be emphasized as the key explanatory framework of biology and as an exemplar of scientific reasoning at its best.[24] Perhaps the forthcoming inclusion of science in the national testing requirement will stimulate more local education leaders to take this responsibility seriously.

Next, we should build upon elements of the educational system that have been shown to work. The American commitment to general education requirements at the baccalaureate level has produced a substantial number of scientifically literate adults—about one in four Americans aged 18 and older. A multivariate analysis found that enrollment in a college-level science course was one of the strongest predictors of adult scientific literacy in the United States. Science educators and faculty at the college and university level need to recognize both the uniqueness of this requirement and its importance to the preservation of democratic government in the 21st century. If every high school graduate were to meet the current minimal definition of scientific literacy, these college and university courses could be used to produce even better informed adults for leadership positions in communities, corporations, and government. In the meantime, these college and university courses provide an essential political safety net for our democratic system.

Also, we must remember that most Americans will learn most of their science after they leave formal schooling. This observation is not a condemnation of formal education, but a simple recognition that the rapid growth of science and technology throughout an individual's lifetime will necessitate learning a good deal of new science. Think about emerging issues such as stem cells, nanotechnology, or global climate change. The vast majority of American adults could not have studied these issues in school because they were not known when the individual was a student. Thus, the task of formal education must be to provide the basic scientific constructs—matter, life, DNA, system, probability, evidence—that are necessary to make sense of new and emerging scientific constructs and issues in the decades after graduation. This recognition should lead formal educators to re-think the long-term consequences of their curriculum and instruction and it should inform adult educators in the media, in libraries and museums, and on the Internet about the need for adult science learning. Informal science centers have also been subject to pressure from creationists and need to take seriously their important role in maintaining scientific integrity.[25]

Finally, science educators at all levels need to do more to incorporate learning about the nature of science and scientific reasoning. If we are to not lose the swing votes to missionary creationists, we need to do a better job explaining what real science is and what it is not. Students need to know how science is different from faith and how it limits itself to testable hypotheses. They need to know why science may not appeal to supernatural explanations and why it is neutral with regard to metaphysical religious beliefs. They need to know how indirect observational evidence can test and confirm hypotheses about things too small or too distant or too far in the past to observe directly. They need to know how the different sciences are interconnected such that one may not simply choose to disbelieve some particular scientific conclusion in isolation. And they need to know the limits of science and when reasoning from the humanities needs to be brought to bear on policy issues. These and other critical elements about the nature of scientific reasoning should not be thought of as a supplement to but rather as basic part of the content of a science course.

If people had a better understanding of how science works, it would not only go a long way towards immunizing them from the fallacious arguments that creationists make but it would also better prepare them to participate as informed citizens in the important decisions that 21st-century science will occasion. Science will be at the center of many key policy questions and science education cannot fail to prepare citizens to meet the challenges that face us. It is thus essential that we resist the attempts from religious extremists to undermine sound science education. This should not be a partisan issue; for our democratic system of government to continue to work, the center must hold.

ENDNOTES

1.   J. D. Miller, "Public Understanding of, and Attitudes Toward, Scientific Research: What we Know and What we Need to Know," *Public Understanding of Science*, 13 (2004): 273-294.

2.   It should be noted that another variant of these questions reduces the number of fundamentalists to 28%. Since the 1980s, the standard question used in the United States and repeated now in more than 40 countries asked a respondent to say whether the statement "Human beings as we know them developed from earlier species of animals" is true or false. Most surveys also offer the respondent an opportunity to say that they do not know or are not sure about this and other knowledge battery items. In 2005, 39% of a national sample of American adults said that this statement was false. Approximately six weeks later, in a follow-up interview, 37% of the same respondents said that they strongly agreed that "Human beings were created by God as whole persons and did not evolve from earlier forms of life," and an additional 25% agreed with the statement, but not strongly. An examination of the responses to these two questions shows that gamma, the ordinal correlation coefficient, for the relationship between the two variables is .75 when aligned in the same direction. Gamma is the ordinal equivalent of r2. Given the amount of error in each of these measurements, the best assumption is that at least one in three American adults is a religious fundamentalist, with another 10% that lean in that direction but do not fully understand the content of the evolution or Intelligent Design controversies.

3.   Miller, E. Scott and S. Okamoto, "Public Acceptance of Evolution," *Science* 313 (August 13, 2006).

4. Robert T. Pennock, "Biology and Religion," in *Cambridge Companion to Philosophy of Biology*, M. Ruse and D. Hull, eds. (Cambridge: Cambridge University Press, 2007), ch. 22.

5. Discovery Institute, *The Wedge Strategy* (Discovery Institute Center for Renewal of Science and Culture, 1999), from www.stephenjaygould.org/ctrl/archive/wedge_document.html [cited 2002].

6. David N. Livingstone, *Darwin's Forgotten Defenders: The Encounter Between Evangelical Theology and Evolutionary Thought* (Edinburgh: Scottish Academy Press, 1987).

7. E. C. Scott, *Evolution vs. Creationism* (Westport, CT: Greenwood Press, 2004); S. M. Barr, "The Design of Evolution," *First Things: A Monthly Journal of Religion & Public Life* 156 (2005): 9-12.

8. Pennock, *Tower of Babel: The Evidence against the New Creationism* (Cambridge, MA: The MIT Press, 1999); Pennock, "Creationism and Intelligent Design," *Annual Review of Genomics and Human Genetics* 4 (2003): 143-163.

9. National surveys were conducted in 1985, 1988, 1990, 1992, 1995, 1997, and 1999 through grants from the National Science Foundation (NSF grants SRS88-07409, SRS90-02467, SRS92-17876, SRS99-06416). All of these studies used telephone interviewing and included approximately 2,000 respondents each year. In 2004 and 2005, national surveys were conducted as a part of an evaluation of two NSF-funded projects conducted by ScienCentral, Inc. (NSF grants ESI-0201155 and ESI-0206184). The 2004 and 2005 studies were conducted online using Knowledge Networks and each study included approximately 2,000 adult respondents. All conclusions are the responsibility of the authors and do not necessarily reflect the views of the National Science Foundation or its staff

10. CBS News Poll, 2005; Gallup, 2004; Harris Interactive, 2005; NBC News Poll, 2005; Scripts Howard, 2005.

11. Miller, Scott and Okamoto (2006).

12. Ibid.

13. Miller, R. Pardo and F. Niwa, Public Perceptions of Science and Technology: A Comparative Study of the European Union, The United States, Japan and Canada (Madrid: BBV Foundation Press, 1997); Miller and L. Kimmel, *Biomedical Communications: Purposes, Audiences, and Strategies* (New York, New York: Academic Press, 2001).

14. *Epperson et al. v. Arkansas*, 393 U.S. 97, 89 S. Ct. 266; 21 L Ed. 2nd 228 (1968).

15. *Kitzmiller et al. v. Dover Area School District et al.* (December 20, 2005).

16. Pennock, "The Pre-Modern Sins of Intelligent Design," in *Oxford Handbook of Science and Religion*, P. Clayton ed. (Oxford: Oxford University Press, 2006).

17. Bush, V. *The Endless Frontier*. Washington, DC: Government Printing Office, 1945.

18. C. Mooney, *The Republican War on Science* (New York: Basic Books, 2005).

19. In the last two years, one political party in Poland has incorporated some of these "family values issues" into their campaigns.

20. J. C. Danforth, "In the Name of Politics," *New York Times*, P.17, 2005.

21. For a description of the 2005 Science News Study, see Miller, E. Augenbraun, J. Schulhof, and Kimmel, "Adult Science Learning from Local Television Newscasts," *Science Communication* 28 (2) (2006): 216-242.

22. *Kitzmiller et al. v. Dover Area School District et al.* (December 20, 2005).

23. Patricia Cohen, "Darwin's Theory sets off a Debate by Conservatives," *The New York Times*, May 5, 2007.

24. Pennock, "On Teaching Evolution and the Nature of Science," in *Evolutionary Science and Society: Educating a New Generation* (Colorado Springs, CO: Biological Sciences Curriculum Study, 2005), J. Cracraft and R. Bybee, eds.

25. Robert, "Scientific Integrity and Science Museums," *Museums and Social Issues* 1 (1) (2006): 7-18.

26. R.C. Davis, *The Public Impact of Science in the Mass Media* (Ann Arbor, MI: Institute for Social Research, University of Michigan, 1958); Miller, "Public Understanding of, and Attitudes Toward, Scientific Research: What we Know and What we Need to Know," *Public Understanding of Science*, 13 (2004): 273-294; Miller, Unpublished tabulations for 2004 (N=1,988) and 2005 (N=2,275).

27. Miller, "Public Understanding of, and Attitudes Toward, Scientific Research: What we Know and What we Need to Know"; Miller, Unpublished tabulations for 2004 (N=1,988) and 2005 (N=2,275).

28. Miller, Unpublished tabulations for 2003, from 10-country Study of Biotechnology (U.S. N=2,066).

29. Miller, "Public Understanding of, and Attitudes Toward, Scientific Research: What we Know and What we Need to Know"; Miller, Scott and Okamoto (2006), 765-766.

30. Miller, Unpublished tabulations for 2003.

31. Miller, "Public Understanding of, and Attitudes Toward, Scientific Research: What we Know and What we Need to Know"; Miller, Scott and Okamoto (2006), 765-766.

32. Miller, Scott and Okamoto (2006), 765-766.

33. Ibid.

34. Ibid.

35. Ibid.

36. Ibid.

2. The Creationist Attack on Science and Secular Society

Daniel G. Blackburn

Introduction

In 1925, John Scopes was put on trial in Dayton, Tennessee, for mentioning the idea of evolution in a biology class that he taught at the local high school. The trial became a media circus, and gained national attention because of what it seemed to represent—a clash of science vs. fundamentalist religion, a conflict between local autonomy and national interests, and an intellectual battle between two great orators, Clarence Darrow and William Jennings Bryan. John Scopes was found guilty and fined, but the verdict was overturned on a technicality— an anticlimactic outcome to the historic conflict. Nevertheless, the trial has grown to mythic proportions, largely through misconceptions promoted by the fictionalized account in the play "Inherit the Wind" and three movie versions based on the play. Readers interested in an accurate historical account of the trial and surrounding events can find one in Larsen's Pulitzer Prize-winning *Summer of the Gods*.[1]

More than 80 years later, the Scopes trial continues to resonate in U.S. society, partly because the reasons for that conflict have never been resolved.[2] Legal challenges continue to be leveled against the teaching of evolution in the public schools.[3] Such challenges are routinely defeated through the judicial system, only to rise again in some other guise or location. Moreover, the social and political movement now known as Creationism has changed and diversified.[4] The movement's tactics have grown more sophisticated, and its ambitions have expanded with its increase in political power.[5] In fact, statements by leading right-wing Creationists have revealed that their goal is nothing less than state-sponsored religion—a right-wing Christian theocracy. Furthermore,

Creationism has grown into an international movement, through which fundamentalists of four major religions oppose the teachings and methods of science.[6] The challenges to free and secular societies are explicit, and anyone who values intellectual freedom, religious freedom, and the separation of church and state should recognize the serious challenge that Creationism represents.

The goals of this review are threefold: (1) to outline the history, beliefs, and activities of the Creationist movement in the U.S.; (2) to explore Creationism's sociopolitical goals and the serious challenge Creationism represents to a free and secular society; and (3) to argue that the idea of a rigid dichotomy between science and religion unnecessarily divides the general public by forcing on them a difficult choice, one that works to the strategic disadvantage of secularism and freedom of thought.

A Brief History of Creationism

Definitive histories of the Creationist movement in the U.S. have been written by Ronald Numbers,[7] and much of what follows is based on his accounts. In the late 1800s and early 1900s, evolution was accepted in scholarly circles by scientists and theologians alike.[8] However, the general public in the U.S. increasingly realized that evolutionary principles and discoveries challenged biblical literalism. The earth's history was being dated in terms of many millions of years, and the evolutionary parade of life could not be reconciled with either the Mosaic creation stories or with a Noachian flood.[9] The growth of the public school system exposed increasing numbers of students to these heretical evolutionary ideas, creating a political backlash. Consequently, during the 1920s, anti-evolution laws were debated by at least 20 U.S. state legislatures, four of which prohibited or condemned the teaching of evolution. Likewise, the increasingly popular "flood geology" provided explanations that were compatible with the Noachian deluge, and laid the groundwork for future decades of so-called "scientific Creationism."[10]

In response to the political controversy, the subject of evolution nearly disappeared from the high school textbooks until the post-Sputnik era. In the early 1960s, evolution was reintroduced as a centerpiece of biology education.[11] Its re-emergence led to two types of responses from the Creationists. One response was the publication of works that claimed a scientific basis for the Genesis stories, including the Great Flood. Their proponents labelled them "creation science" in hopes of gaining them greater intellectual respectability.[12] The other response was political and in the early 1980s resulted in legislative initiatives in 26 states to mandate "equal time" for Creation science.[13] In general, the legislative initiatives were rebuffed by the judicial system on the grounds that they violated the First Amendment's clause against state establishment of religion. However, these events paralleled a dramatic shift among practicing Christians toward beliefs that the earth was formed only a few thousand years ago. The shift is unprecedented and hard to account for on socioeconomic grounds.[14]

The 1990s brought a host of new initiatives, including legislation to mandate the teaching of evidence against evolution, and to require that evolution be taught with the disclaimer that it is not factual but "just a theory."[15] In Tennessee, teachers who failed to label evolution "a theory" were to be subject to termination. The Tennessee proposal showed a basic misunderstanding of how scientists use the word "theory"—as a synonym of "principle" or scientific "law." Thus, the legislative proposal's goal was to require that evolution be treated in the schools as an uncorroborated hypothesis, but its very wording codified ignorance about scientific concepts. During the 1990s, Creationist beliefs were added to Republican Party platforms in a number of states. Local school districts removed or pasted together textbook pages that dealt with evolution, and beliefs about evolution became a battleground in many school board elections.[16]

The "Intelligent Design" (ID) movement is the latest manifestation of Creationism. Intelligent Design Creationists commonly stop short of publicly promoting biblical creation—hence its designations as "repackaged Creationism" and "Creationism's Trojan horse."[17] The central assumption of ID is that living organisms are far too complex to be products of evolution, and therefore that they must have been created in their present form by a Grand Designer.[18] The nature and identity of the "designer(s)" commonly are left unstated, and in theory might be space aliens, time travelers, or mischievous demons. However, public statements and private documents of ID proponents and organizations leave no doubt that the "designer" they have in mind is the Christian deity.[19] As Pennock[20] notes, in ID documents and websites, the term "Intelligent Designer" is widely considered to be "the politically correct term for God."

A recent court case in Pennsylvania[21] tested the constitutionality of a school district's requirement that Intelligent Design must be presented in the classroom.[22] Teachers were required to read to science students a statement about ID and to recommend the Creationist textbook *Of Pandas and People*—a requirement with which the teachers refused to comply. The school district lost the case on the basis of its violation of the establishment clause of the constitution. In his memorandum opinion, Judge John E. Jones III wrote that Intelligent Design "is not science and cannot be adjudged a valid, accepted scientific theory as it has failed to publish in peer-reviewed journals, engage in research and testing, and gain acceptance in the scientific community." Noting that "ID cannot uncouple itself from its Creationist, and thus religious, antecedents," he labelled the school district's ID requirement "breathtaking inanity."[23]

The Creationist Spectrum, and Beyond

Far from a monolithic movement, Creationism includes a full spectrum of conflicting perspectives that grade into more conventional forms of theism.[24] One major distinction can be made according to beliefs about age of the earth and the universe. "Young-Earth Creationists" (YECs) believe that the earth's age is measurable in thousands of years, a view taken from a literal reading of the Old Testament. They contrast with "Old-Earth Creationists," who consider the earth to be millions of years old. Some YECs (such as the group known as the Missouri Lutherans) are geocentrists, who believe that the sun orbits the earth.[25] Others are "flat-earthers," such as members of the International Flat Earth Society, a group that has its headquarters in Lancaster, California.[26] The beliefs of both groups reflect a traditional Hebrew cosmology, in which the earth was thought to be a disk floating on water, and the heavens were held up by a domelike firmament to which was attached the sun, moon, and stars.[27] This firmament separated the waters of the heavens from those of the earth, and the water poured through it at the time of Noah's flood. Contemporary YECs claim that dinosaurs co-existed with humans in Edenic times, when all animals were herbivores; they became carnivorous when "sin" entered the world. Such ideas are promoted in children's books—and in Creationist museums, such as the 27 million dollar Creation Museum that was recently opened in Petersburg, Kentucky.[28]

"Old-Earth Creationists" agree on an ancient origin for the earth; however, they hold different views about whether the actual creation of life took six literal days or six longer time periods. Some who posit a six-day creation reconcile their views with the accepted age of the earth by invoking an ancient, pre-Adamic creation that was destroyed prior to the creation described in Genesis 2.[29]

"Progressive Creationists" accept the existence of limited forms of evolution within basic types formed through special creation. Under their interpretation, members of (for example) the cat family (Felidae) could be accepted as having evolved from a specially created feline prototype.[30] These beliefs allow Progressive Creationists to accept the overwhelming evidence for microevolution (change within populations) as well as fossil evidence for modifications within particular groups. However, they invoke the deity for macroevolutionary events and for special creation of the ancestral prototypes. Although many proponents of these views accept the idea of an ancient earth, the influential George McCready Price (1870-1963) combined young-earth Creationism with limited forms of progressive evolution.[31] However, to strict Creationists of the traditional variety, acceptance of any form of evolution is anathema.

Proponents of Intelligent Design[32] (ID) may adopt any of a range of views on history and age of life on earth, but commonly they are OECs. Intelligent Design Creationists (IDCs) hold differing beliefs about the efficacy and scope of evolution.[33] However, they are united by the belief that natural processes cannot account for the history and diversity of life. Most who have been publicly identified with the ID movement accept a form of God-directed evolution.[34] If their perspective were simply theological, it would not be controversial. However, the movement masks its religious underpinnings, motives, and goals in order to have its theological views taught in science classrooms as fact. Because proponents of ID commonly allow for an earth of great antiquity and accept the existence of evolution, more traditional Creationists oppose their views.

One further perspective to be recognized is a widespread view that can be termed "theistic evolution." Because its adherents accept evolution, they are not "Creationists" under common use of that term. Such individuals believe that the evolutionary process was the means by which God effected life's creation,[35] although they differ in the extent to which they believe the deity intervened in the process. Theistic evolution is a doctrine implicitly or explicitly supported by mainstream churches. It has had strong adherents among scientists, particularly from the 1860s through the first three decades of the 20th century.[36]

Methodological materialism is intrinsic to science. Therefore, competent professional scientists can hold a diversity of personal religious views while formulating their scientific explanations solely in terms of natural phenomena and causes. Among several reasons that Creationism (in its several manifestations) is not science are the following: that it invokes supernatural causes as direct explanations of natural phenomena in the context of scientific teaching and research; that it fails to deal in falsifiable (disprovable) hypotheses; and that it begins with conclusions for which it seeks confirmatory evidence.[37] In contrast, scientific methodology seeks only to disprove (falsify) hypotheses. As Gould[38] stated "[t]he fundamentalists, by 'knowing' the answers before they start [examining evolution], and then forcing nature into the straitjacket of their discredited preconceptions, lie outside the domain of science—or of any honest intellectual inquiry."

The Assault on Knowledge and Rationality

The content of Creationist beliefs has been documented and analyzed in numerous books and scholarly papers by scientists, philosophers, and historians.[39] Creationism's claims have repeatedly been shown to be intellectually vacuous, and its tactics, ethically indefensible. To the many scientists (including the present author) who have had their words distorted in order to discredit evolution, it appears that no deception is too base, as long as it serves the Creationist cause. Outlined below are ways in which Creationism conflicts with knowledge and methodologies of scholarly inquiry.

Life Sciences

To understand the seriousness of the Creationist attack requires an appreciation of the important position evolution occupies in modern biology. Evolution is central to the life sciences, the overarching framework that makes biology a coherent discipline, rather than a collection of miscellaneous facts about obscure organisms.[40] Most everything we have learned about biology relates either to mechanisms or to manifestations of evolution. Thus, as often noted in the life sciences literature, without evolution, information from the entire spectrum of biological disciplines would make little or no sense. Among the biological disciplines that rely on the principles of evolution are anatomy, physiology, immunology, developmental biology, biochemistry, genetics, molecular biology, cell biology, neuroscience, botany, zoology, microbiology, systematics, ethology, and ecology. The list encompasses all of the life sciences, including disciplines that at one time seemed to bear little relationship to evolution.

For example, in the early decades of the 20th century, information about transmission (Mendelian) genetics seemed to be difficult to reconcile with natural selection. However, by the "Modern Synthesis" of the 1940s, genetics not only was seen as compatible with natural selection, it was recognized as the key to understanding how evolution works.[41] Likewise, molecular genetics was developed in the 1970s with limited reference to evolutionary phenomena, yet evolution is now central to the discipline. Evolutionary principles account for genetic diversity as well as commonalties, and explain otherwise inexplicable phenomena such as "junk DNA" and "fossil genes" that have lost their functions evolutionarily.[42]

To disregard evolution is to discount nearly everything of significance that we have learned in biology. In fact, to do so can be a life-or-death matter, since ignoring evolution would rob us of the powerful explanatory power of evolutionary principles in human medicine.[43] To cite one of many examples: had medical professionals been familiar with the rapid effects of natural selection, perhaps we would not have so quickly selected for resistant microbial strains through indiscriminate use of weak doses of antibiotics. Evolutionary principles also help explain such medical phenomena as sickle cell anemia, lactose intolerance, fever, and schizophrenia.

Physical Sciences

For Creationism to be correct, not only would the precepts and methods of biology have to be fundamentally wrong, but those of other scientific disciplines would have to be incorrect as well. Chemistry and physics provide well-established analytical procedures by which we can determine the age of fossils and the rocks in which they are found; such procedures are based on known rates of isotope decay and element replacement. Young-earth Creationism would require basic laws of chemistry and physics to be invalid, and would require that the methods of these fields falsely lead scientists to infer that the world is much older than the ~6000 years that Archbishop James Ussher calculated in 1654. Geology has allowed us to reconstruct the history of our planet over the past 4 billion years, and has documented the natural forces and phenomena that have produced mountains, canyons, lakes, oceans, and drifting continents. Against the vast scientific evidence accumulated from the Renaissance, through the Scientific Revolution, to the present, lie the claims of YECs, who believe that major geological features resulted from recent biblical events. As an example, Creationists insist that everything from fossil organisms to the Grand Canyon resulted from Noah's flood. Their claims are now disseminated through the U.S. National Parks Service.[44]

The field of astronomy offers another example. Astronomy has revealed that our sun is one of countless stars in the Milky Way galaxy, which in turn is one of countless galaxies in a universe far more vast than our imaginations can ever contemplate. Against the information provided by several centuries of telescopes trained on the skies from Copernicus and Galileo onward are the claims of geocentrists, flat-earthers, and others with minds limited by dogma. In May 2007, a massive stellar explosion was visible on earth, representing the largest supernova recorded in human history. It resulted from the explosion of an enormous star designated SN 2006gy in the galaxy NGC 1260, over 240 million light years away.[45] The explosion that produced it occurred towards the beginning of our earth's Triassic period, back before the earliest dinosaurs, birds, and mammals. Young-earth Creationists who claim the universe to be no older than a few thousand years must assume that this explosion never occurred, and that light rays that fool us into thinking that it had occurred were created in position as if they had traveled more than 99.99% of the distance toward our planet. YECs would have us ignore the evidence of our senses and the products of our intellects in favor of unquestioning acceptance of ancient cosmologies of pre-scientific peoples.

Social Sciences and Humanities

Creationist claims also are incompatible with knowledge gained from the humanities and social sciences. For example, the field of anthropology has much to say about the prehistory of our species, and about hominid ancestors dating as far back as 7 million years ago. Using the tools of molecular genetics, anthropologists and biologists are reconstructing the peopling of the globe over the past 100,000 years.[46] Likewise, studies in comparative linguistics have allowed reconstruction of the evolution of languages and their spread around the globe during this same time period.[47] Needless to say, neither the Mosaic account of Babel nor a post-Noachian diaspora have been corroborated. The fields of history and archaeology have yielded challenging insights into events and ancient cultures mentioned in biblical accounts.[48] The field of psychology has provided great insight into the nature of gender differences, including those that are fully consistent with evolutionary principles and predictions.[49] Likewise, the interdisciplinary field of neuroscience has provided insight into the nature of consciousness, "free will," and the biological basis of religious belief,[50] while allowing detailed reconstruction of the deep evolutionary history of the components of the human brain—features widely shared with other mammals.

Methodology and Epistemology

Not only is Creationism inconsistent with a vast corpus of factual knowledge, it also is incompatible with the methods through which knowledge is obtained. Science deals in testable and tested propositions. Any scientific statement must be able to be disproved (falsified), and in order to be accepted, it must survive rigorous attempts to disprove it.[51] By contrast, religious and political dogmas begin with the presumption of validity, and consider attempts to question them as heretical and forbidden. When such dogmas are challenged, they can be enforced through the full power of the state—to the detriment of freedom of thought, expression, and investigation.

Why Evolution?

In light of the above, Creationists' particular focus on biological evolution may not be immediately evident. This focus cannot be attributed solely to conflict with biblical creation accounts. After all, these same accounts conflict with much that is known and taught in the fields of geology, physics, astronomy, archeology, history, and other fields. We do not see legislative initiatives to prohibit the teaching of heliocentrism, continental drift, or the nature of stars, nor do school board members agitate for the teaching of the Firmament Model, or for the Tower of Babel theory of languages.[52] The focus on evolution also cannot be attributed solely to difficulty in understanding the concept itself. Science leads us to believe facts far more difficult to comprehend and believe: that each of us developed from a single microscopic cell; that human beings are made of the same elements as are found in rocks, dirt, and trees; that physical objects are composed of invisible particles whose existence at any given place and time is a matter of probability; and that the earth's sun is a medium-sized star among countless trillions in a limitless universe.

Evolution may be a special target of Creationist ire because it holds that humans resulted from natural, mechanistic processes, and that they share a common ancestry with other animals. Just as the Copernican revolution showed that the earth is not the center of the universe, Darwinian evolution seemingly deposed humankind (in the public mind) from an exalted position as the pinnacle and endpoint of a goal-directed creation.[53] It also came to imply that human behaviors, and even human morality and altruism, have naturalistic origins and pre-human antecedents.[54] However, evidence supports a more insidious explanation for the Creationist focus—that the attack on evolution is a useful tactic in an ambitious sociopolitical agenda. Recent Creationist writings and private documents are explicit about the tactic of using evolution to divide the U.S. public for political motives.[55]

In sum, although the subject of evolution draws special opposition, Creationism is far more than an attack on a single specialty within biology. For Creationism to be true, most of what we have learned from the natural sciences, and much that we have learned in the humanities and social sciences, would have to be untrue. Thus Creationism implicitly is an assault on knowledge and on rationality, and a movement with explicit political motives and goals.

The Attack on Secularism

The Politics of Creationism

Creationism is a sociopolitical movement that actively seeks to replace knowledge gained over the course of many centuries with an extremist form of religion. Although the U.S. has been a bastion of Creationism for over a century, the movement has become worldwide in scope. Islamic and Hindu versions are gaining increasing support.[56] Throughout the history of the Creationist movement, one overarching objective has been limiting the dissemination and acceptance of ideas of biological evolution. For most of the 20th century, the subject of evolution was downplayed or ignored in public school textbooks and curricula in the U.S., through local control of school curricula and legislative initiatives launched at state and local levels.

Whether for these or other reasons, the U.S. populace remains woefully ignorant of the basic outlines of evolutionary processes and events and the overwhelming evidence for their validity. Far from being a tiny fringe minority, individuals who accept the precepts of Young-Earth Creationism make up a plurality of the U.S. adult population. In a poll conducted by Princeton Survey Research Associates International,[57] 48% of the respondents agreed with the statement "God created humans pretty much in the present form at one time within the last 10,000 years or so." (Among evangelical Protestants, the figure was 73%.) Of all the respondents, 30% supported a God-directed evolution, and 13% said that evolution was not directed by a deity. These results are consistent with similar surveys dating back to the early 1980s.[58]

From another set of surveys, supported by the National Science Foundation, Miller and Pennock[59] report weak support in the U.S. for the idea of human evolution, support that has declined from 45% to 40% between 1985 and 2005. The 2005 survey revealed that 28% of the respondents believed that humans lived at the same time as dinosaurs, with another 22% indicating that they were not sure (only 51% disagreed with the statement—and one might wonder how many of those disbelieved in dinosaurs). Such poll results might be understandable had they come from a population under control of a theocratic regime, or from a Third World nation where books are scarce and higher education is a luxury. In fact, the U.S. is extraordinarily anomalous among developed nations. In a group of 34 countries primarily from Europe and Asia, the U.S. ranked next to last in acceptance of evolution; only Turkey ranked lower.[60] Whatever its causes, the widespread disbelief in evolution in the U.S. offers fertile ground for Creationist attempts to limit its presentation in the public schools.

On the political front, Creationism has grown into a well-financed and powerful movement. Its supporters extend to the highest reaches of the U.S. government. Among those sympathetic to Creationist goals have been two of the last four U.S. Presidents, many state governors and state and federal legislators, and at least two justices of the Supreme Court.[61] With evangelical religion having gained significant control over one of the two national political parties,[62] we may soon see a time when a Creationist pledge is expected of contenders for political office, just as dutiful pledges of religious belief are now implicitly required of serious candidates for Congress and the U.S. presidency.

Discovery Institute

One major supporter of the Intelligent Design movement is the Discovery Institute (DI), an association with an annual budget in excess of 4.2 million dollars.[63] DI pronouncements deny explicit religious motives and affiliations, and claim that Intelligent Design is a legitimate scientific principle. However, a *New York Times* investigation reported that most of the Institute's fellows are fundamentalist or evangelical Christians, and most of its financial support comes from organizations whose mission statements include explicit religious goals.[64] The *Times* investigation reported that $3.6 million in fellowships had yielded 50 books on ID, along with numerous articles and two television documentaries. Recently, the DI has hired the public relations firm that launched the negative "Swift Boat" television commercials against the Democratic candidate for the U.S. Presidency in the 2004 elections.[65]

The Discovery Institute's famous "Wedge Document," leaked to the Internet in 1999,[66] states that the DI's goal is "to reverse the stifling dominance of the materialist worldview," and "to replace it with a science consonant with Christian and theistic convictions." The manifesto proclaims that DI "seeks nothing less than the overthrow of materialism and its cultural legacies…" and "to replace materialistic explanations with the theistic understanding that nature and human beings are created by God." Because science deals only in materialistic explanations, such objectives are entirely antithetical to science. The Wedge Document also outlined a "Strategic Plan" whose goals included making ID "the dominant perspective in science," something that would "permeate our religious, cultural, moral and political life." Clearly, the Institute does not intend to contribute to the growth of scientific knowledge, but rather to advance a reactionary political and religious agenda.

Thus, the goals of the contemporary Creationist movement in the U.S. are not limited to questions over the teaching of evolution. The explicit goals are far more broad and insidious: to supplant science with religious dogma in the public schools, and to displace secularism with religion in the political realm. To people unfamiliar with science, and who operate under the misconception that evolution is scientifically controversial, "Intelligent Design" may seem quite attractive as a (purportedly) scientific principle that supports religion. Consequently, if the claims of ID can be made to appear legitimate (not a difficult proposition to those who think that dinosaurs once cavorted with human children), then it may appear unfair that it is not taught in the public schools. Under the circumstances, the issue easily devolves into one of local vs. state or federal control of the school curriculum.

Implications

It is important to consider what would ensue if the teaching of ID or other forms of Creationism were to be mandated in the public schools through government intervention. Of course it is not illegal for individual teachers to teach Creationism at present, nor is it illegal for evolution to be ignored, distorted, or discounted in science classrooms. As other commentators on these issues have noted, the teaching of bad science is not itself unconstitutional.

However, if the teaching of evolution were to be made illegal, or if "equal time" for Creationism were to be required in the classroom, the government would be obligated to enforce the laws against those teachers and school administrators unwilling to comply. Public schools could be swept of qualified teachers and administrators, as willingness to teach "Creation science" becomes a requirement for employment and school accreditation. Teachers who refuse to compromise their principles and intellectual freedom would likely lose their jobs or leave the profession; others would stand on principle even if it meant prosecution. Court cases could abound, as the full weight of the law was brought to bear, and those educators thought to be in violation could face arrest, trial, and imprisonment. No reason exists to suppose that efforts to control the teaching of evolution would be confined to the high school level. Science faculty at state universities, which are indirectly controlled by state legislatures, could also be subject to prosecution. Private colleges and universities also could be affected, given their reliance on state and federal funds, grants, and sponsored loans to students.

The above scenario may seem implausible, but we are now dangerously close to seeing it actualized. If widespread efforts to legislate what is taught in science classrooms were to succeed, the judicial system would be required to uphold all laws not found to be unconstitutional. Given the close votes in key court cases, a continued shift in the judiciary (an explicit goal of the radical right) could bring to bear the full power of the state—to investigate, arrest, prosecute, fine, and imprison—against teachers and scholars. Viewed in this context, Creationism can be seen as the vanguard of a theocratic movement, and its attack on public school curricula part of an explicit assault on secular society, free inquiry, and academic freedom. Creationism arguably represents the most public manifestation of a broad-based and well-financed effort to replace secular society with a theocratic state.[67] Clearly, in this political conflict, the stakes are very high.

Simplistic Dichotomies and Political Polarization

As discussed above, Creationist goals are much more ambitious than simply discrediting a particular academic discipline. Evolution, however, offers a visible target because of its perceived incompatibility with fundamentalist religious beliefs. Some incompatibilities are undeniable; after all, a literal reading of Genesis cannot be reconciled with what we know about the history of life and the origins of our species. Nevertheless, theists who take a more scholarly approach to biblical writings have historically had little difficulty reconciling their religion with their knowledge of science. Indeed, during the past 150 years, many religious establishments in the U.S., England, and Europe have readily accommodated the facts and principles of evolution.[68] Biologists and philosophers of science also have ranged widely in their personal beliefs about religion, from devout Christians through professed atheists and agnostics.[69]

The perennial issue of whether "science" and "religion" are in conflict is not resolvable in any global sense, because the answer depends so strongly on the specific facts and beliefs under consideration. Facile assurances that science and religion are easy to reconcile[70] tend to be intellectually unsatisfying, and fail to recognize areas of undeniable disagreement. Nevertheless, the 19th century metaphor of "warfare" between science and religion[71] has long since given way to nuanced perspectives that are based on more careful, and less ideological, readings of history. Such perspectives recognize that over the centuries, "science" and "religion" have not been static entities nor mutually exclusive enterprises; that science and religion have had complex and changing relationships; and that much of science was developed with religious motives and with the support of religious institutions.[72] Thus, conflicts and areas of consensus between science and religion turn out to be manifestations of particular cultures at particular points in history.

The diversity of views of individual scientists and theists and the complex historical relationship between science and religion argue against viewing these two human enterprises as intrinsically and diametrically opposed. Furthermore, strident attacks on religion from the scientific camp[73] risk alienating sympathetic theists by conflating their views with extreme forms of religiosity. They thereby tend to force on the general public a choice between two polar extremes that most are reluctant and ill-equipped to make. Significantly, this is the same choice that Creationists have promoted, and for good reason. With the percentage of atheists and agnostics numbering in the single digits according to U.S. surveys, such a draconian choice is one from which Creationism stands most to benefit. Both principle and pragmatism therefore argue for mutual tolerance between the institutions of science and religion, and much more is to be gained by cooperation and respectful discourse than conflict.

In sum, the above analysis argues that Creationist attacks are more than an attempt to force the teaching of religion as science; they are part of a broad assault on rationality and on secular institutions. All individuals who value freedom of thought, freedom of religion, and the separation of church and state (theists and non-theists alike) have every reason to resist this dangerous intrusion of religion into the public sphere, for the sake of secular society and its institutions.

ENDNOTES

1. Edward J. Larsen, *Summer of the Gods: The Scopes Trial and America's Continuing Debate over Science and Religion* (New York: Basic Books, 1997).

2. Ronald L. Numbers, *Darwinism Comes to America* (Cambridge, MA: Harvard University Press, 1998).

3. Eugenie C. Scott, "Anti-evolutionism and Creationism in the United States," *Annual Review of Anthropology* 26 (1997): 263-289; see Numbers, 1998; Randy Olson, *Flock of Dodos* (Documentary Educational Resources: Boston, MA, 2006), documentary film.

4. Numbers, *From Scientific Creationism to Intelligent Design* (Cambridge, MA: Harvard University Press, 2006); Scott, "Creationism, Ideology, and Science," *Annals of the New York Academy of Sciences* 775 (1996): 505–522; see also Scott, 1997; Scott, *Evolution vs. Creationism* (Berkeley, CA: University of California Press, 2004).

5. Barbara Forrest and Paul R. Gross, *Creationism's Trojan Horse: The Wedge of Intelligent Design* (New York: Oxford University Press, 2004).

6. Simon Coleman and Leslie Carlin, eds., *The Cultures of Creationism: Anti-Evolution in English-Speaking Countries* (Burlington, VT: Ashgate Publishing, 2004); Ümit Sayin and Aykut Kence, "Islamic Scientific Creationism: A New Challenge in Turkey," *Resources of the National Center for Science Education* 19 (6) (1999): 18-20, 25-29.

7. Numbers, *The Creationists: The Evolution of Scientific Creationism* (Berkeley, CA: University of California Press, 1992); see also Numbers, 2006; Raymond A. Eve and Francis B. Harrold, *The Creationist Movement in Modern America* (Boston: Twayne Publishers, 1990); see also Scott, 1997.

8. Peter J. Bowler, *Reconciling Science and Religion: The Debate in Early 20th Century Britain* (Chicago: University of Chicago Press, 2001); James R. Moore, *The Post-Darwinian Controversies* (Cambridge, MA: Cambridge University Press, 1981).

9. Charles C. Gillispie, *Genesis and Geology: The Impact of Scientific Discoveries upon Religious Beliefs in the Decades before Darwin* (New York: Harper and Row, 1956).

10. See Numbers, 1992.

11. Ibid.

12. See Numbers, 1998.

13. Scott, "The Struggle for the Schools," *Natural History* 103 (7) (1994): 10-13. The "equal time" mandate reportedly was opposed by some supporters of Creationism in Oklahoma because it would have required the teaching of evolution, a subject not being taught at that time. See Numbers, 1998.

14. Otis Dudley Duncan and Claudia Geist. The creationists: how many, who, and where? Reports of the National Center for Science Education 24 (5) (2004): 26-33.; also see Numbers, 1998.

15. See Scott, 1997.

16. See Numbers, 1998.

17. See Forrest and Gross, 2004.

18. Michael Behe, *Darwin's Black Box: The Biochemical Challenge to Evolution* (New York: Free Press, 1996).

19. E.g., Forrest and Gross, 2004; Olson, 2006; Jon D. Miller and Robert T. Pennock, this volume (2008).

20. Pennock, *Tower of Babel: The Evidence against the New Creationism* (Cambridge, MA: MIT Press, 1999).

21. *Kitzmiller et al. v. Dover Area School District, et al.,* Case No. 04cv2688. All documents of the court case are available at the National Center for Science Education website, "Evolution, Education, and the Law": http://www2.ncseweb.org/wp/.

    They are also available online at the ACLU website: http://www.aclupa.org/legal/legaldocket/intelligentdesigncase/.

22. See Olson, 2006; Miller and Pennock, 2008.

23. *Kitzmiller v. Dover.*

24. Mark Isaak, "What is Creationism?" *Talk Origins Archive* (May 30, 2007), http://www.talkorigins.org/faqs/wic.html; Numbers, 2006; Pennock, 1999; Scott, 1997; Scott, "The Creation/Evolution Continuum," *Reports of the National Center for Science Education* 19 (4) (1999): 16–23.

25. See Numbers, 1998; Scott, 1999.

26. Scott, 1997.

27. See Scott, 1999.

28. Gordon Slack, "Inside the Creation Museum," *Salon* magazine, June 1, 2007, http://www.salon.com/news/feature/2007/05/ 31/ creation_museum/index.html.

29. Scott, 1997.

30. Numbers, 1992; Scott, 1997.

31. Numbers, 1992.

32. Parallel grammatical usage would suggest that such proponents be called "Intelligent Design-ers." However, the individuals described would deny implications of the noun, and some of their opponents, the adjective. Hence the term "Intelligent Design Creationists," which is both accurate and descriptive.

33. Pennock, ed., *Intelligent Design Creationism and its Critics: Philosophical, Theological, and Scientific Perspectives* (Cambridge, MA: MIT Press, 2001); see Scott, 1999.

34. See, e.g., Behe, 1996; see Olson, 2006.

35. Bowler, *Reconciling Science and Religion: The Debate in Early 20th Century Britain*; see Moore, 1981.

36. Bowler, *Evolution: The History of an Idea* (Berkeley, CA: University of California Press, 1984); see Bowler, 2001.

37. See Pennock, 1999, 2001; Michael Ruse, *The Evolution-Creation Struggle* (Cambridge, MA: Harvard University Press, 2005).

38. Stephen Jay Gould, "An Essay on a Pig Roast," in *Bully For Brontosaurus* (New York: Norton, 1991) 432-447.

39. E.g., Niles Eldredge, *The Triumph of Evolution and the Failure of Creationism* (New York: W.H. Freeman, 2001); Philip Kitcher, *Living with Darwin: Evolution, Design, and the Future of Faith* (New York: Oxford University Press, 2006); see Numbers, 2006; see Pennock, 1999; Pennock, ed., *Intelligent Design Creationism and its Critics: Philosophical, Theological, and Scientific Perspectives* (Cambridge, MA: MIT Press, 2001); Mark Perakh, *Unintelligent Design* (Amherst, NY: Prometheus Books, 2003); Andrew J. Petto and Laurie R. Godfrey, *Scientists Confront Intelligent Design and Creationism* (New York: Norton, 2007); see Ruse, 2005; see Scott, 2004; George C. Williams, *The Pony Fish's Glow and Other Clues to Plan and Purpose in Nature* (New York: Basic Books, 1997).

40. Ernst Mayr, *The Growth of Biological Thought* (Cambridge, MA: Harvard University Press, 1981).

41. See Mayr, 1981; Mayr and William B. Provine, eds., *The Modern Synthesis: Perspectives on the Unification of Biology* (Cambridge, MA: Harvard University Press, 1980).

42. Sean B. Carroll, *The Making of the Fittest: DNA and the Ultimate Forensic Record of Evolution* (New York: W.W. Norton, 2006).

43. Randolph N. Nesse and George C. Williams, *Why We Get Sick: The New Science of Darwinian Medicine* (New York: Vintage Books, 1996).

44. Glenn Branch, "Creationists and the Grand Canyon," *The Humanist*, March/April 64 (2) (2004): 5–6, 47; NCSE, "Renewed Concern about Creationism at Grand Canyon National Park," Resource of the National Center for Science Education, May 30, 2007, http://www.ncseweb.org/resources/news/2007/US/699_renewed_concern_about_creation_1_4_2007.asp.

45. NASA, "NASA's Chandra sees Brightest Supernova Ever," National Aeronautics and Space Administration report, June 1, 2007, http://www.nasa.gov/mission_pages/chandra/ news/chandra_bright_supernova.html.

46. Luigi Luca Cavalli-Sforza, *Genes, People, and Languages* (New York: North Point Press, 2000); Steve Olson, *Mapping Human History: Discovering the Past through our Genes* (Boston: Houghton Mifflin, 2002); S. Oppenheimer, *The Real Eve: Modern Man's Journey out of Africa* (New York: Carroll and Graf, 2004).

47. See Cavalli-Sforza, 2000.

48. Israel Finkelstein and Neil Asher Silberman, *The Bible Unearthed* (New York: Free Press, 2001); Finkelstein and Silberman, *David and Solomon: In Search of the Bible's Sacred Kings and the Roots of the Western Tradition* (New York: Free Press, 2006).

49. David M. Buss, *The Evolution of Desire: The Strategies of Human Mating* (New York: Harper Collins, 1994).

Geoffrey Miller, *The Mating Mind* (New York: Anchor Books, 2001).

50. Daniel C. Dennett, *Consciousness Explained* (Boston: Little, Brown and Company, 1991); Dennett, *Freedom Evolves* (New York: Viking Press, 2003); Dennett, *Breaking the Spell: Religion as a Natural Phenomenon* (New York: Viking Press, 2006).

51. Karl R. Popper, *The Logic of Scientific Discovery* (New York: Basic Books, 1959); Peter B. Medawar, *The Art of the Soluble* (London: Methuen, 1967); Medawar, *The Limits of Science* (New York: Harper & Row, 1984).

52. See Pennock, 1999.

53. Loren C. Eiseley, *Darwin's Century: Evolution and the Men who Discovered It* (New York: Doubleday, 1958).

54. Matt Ridley, *The Origins of Virtue: Human Instincts and the Evolution of Cooperation* (New York: Viking Press, 1996).

55. See Forrest and Gross, 2004.

56. See Coleman and Carlin, 2004; *The Economist*, "In the Beginning: The Debate over Creation and Evolution, Once Most Conspicuous in America, is Going Global," April 19, 2007, http://www.economist.com/world/displaystory.cfm?story_id=9036706; see Isaak, 2000; NCSE, "Creationism News from Around the World," National Center for Science Education, November 2, 2006, http://www.ncseweb.org/resources/news/2006/XX/961_creationism_news_from_around_t_11_2_2006.asp.

See Pennock, 1999; see Sayin and Kence, 1999.

57. *Newsweek*, "Newsweek Poll: Religious Beliefs," March 31, 2007, http://www.msnbc.msn.com/id/17875540/site/newsweek/.

58. See Duncan and Geist, 2004; NCSE, "A New Creationism/Evolution Poll, but Few Surprises," Resource of the National Center for Science Education, May 30, 2007, http://www.ncseweb.org/resources/news/2007/US/20_a_new_creationismevolution_po_4_4_2007.asp.

59. See Miller and Pennock, 2008.

60. Ibid.

61. See Forrest and Gross, 2004; Stephen Jay Gould, "Justice Scalia's Misunderstanding," in Gould, *Bully for Brontosaurus* (New York: Norton, 1991), 448-460.

62. See Miller and Pennock, 2008; *Newsweek*, 2007.

63. Discovery Institute website.

64. Jodi Wilgoren, Jack Begg, David Bernstein, and Alain Delaquérière, "Politicized Scholars put Evolution on the Defensive," *New York Times*, August 21, 2005.

65. See Olson, 2006.

66. See Forrest and Gross, 2004.

67. Kevin P. Phillips, *American Theocracy: The Peril and Politics of Radical Religion, Oil, and Borrowed Money in the 21st Century* (New York: Viking Press, 2006).

68. See Bowler, 1984, 2001; see Moore, 1981.

69. Francis A. Collins, *The Language of God: A Scientist Presents Evidence for Belief* (New York: Free Press, 2007); Richard C. Dawkins, *The God Delusion* (Boston: Houghton Mifflin, 2006); William S. Provine. "Progress in Evolution and Meaning in Life." In: *Evolutionary Progress* (Matthew H. Nitecki, ed.), pp. 49-74. (Chicago, University of Chicago Press, 1989); see Dennett, 2006; see Provine, 1991.

70. E.g., Gould, *Rocks of Ages: Science and Religion in the Fullness of Life* (New York: Ballantine, 1999).

71. John W. Draper, *History of the Conflict between Religion and Science* (New York: Appleton and Company, 1874); Andrew Dickson White, *A History of the Warfare of Science and Theology in Christendom* (New York: Appleton and Company, 1896).

72. See Moore, 1981; Numbers, "Science and Religion," *Osiris, 2nd series,* 1 (1985): 59-80 (1985); Richard Tarnas, *The Passion of the Western Mind: Understanding the Ideas that have Shaped our World View* (New York: Ballantine Books, 1991).

73. See Dawkins, 2006; Sam Harris, *Letter to a Christian Nation* (New York: Knopf, 2006).

3. Evolution Education and the Science-Religion Conflict: Dispatches from a Philosophical Correspondent

Austin Dacey

C harles Darwin tried to avoid it. Richard Dawkins, perhaps Darwin's greatest expositor, couldn't resist it. Darwin wrote,

> It appears to me (whether rightly or wrongly) that direct arguments against Christianity & theism produce hardly any effect on the public; & freedom of thought is best promoted by the gradual illumination of men's minds which follow[s] from the advance of science. It has, therefore, been always my object to avoid writing on religion, & I have confined myself to science.[1]

Dawkins wrote *The God Delusion*, a 400-page polemic on the irrationality of supernatural theism, and the absurdity and immorality of much traditional religion. Perhaps it should not surprise that the most commercially successful book by Dawkins is also the book worst received by his colleagues in science and science education. Although many reviewers spoke admiringly of his intellectual integrity, they criticized him for what they regarded as a confrontational, combative stance on religion.

Throughout the work, Dawkins describes a conflict between science and religion that has been decisively won, in his view, by science. As the scientific picture of the world has grown more credible, especially since Darwin, the religious picture of the world has grown less credible. Dawkins uses evolutionary reasoning to argue that "there almost certainly is no God":

> This book will advocate an alternative view: *any creative intelligence, of sufficient complexity to design anything, comes into existence only as the end product of an extended process of gradual evolution*. Creative

51

intelligences, being evolved, necessarily arrive late in the universe, and therefore cannot be responsible for designing it. God, in the sense defined, is a delusion....

The reception of *The God Delusion* was part of a larger ongoing debate in America, the United Kingdom, and elsewhere about the state of public understanding of science and science education. The debate is particularly intense in the United States, where close to half the public accepts young-earth Creationism,[2] and where well-organized and well-funded groups of religiously motivated activists continue to agitate against the teaching of evolution and for the inclusion of Creationist ideas in public school science curricula. In 2005, Pew Forum polling found that 64% of American adults favored the teaching of Creationism alongside evolution in public schools.[3] Moreover, Creationist activists often use the argument that evolutionary science is essentially atheistic and therefore that its inclusion in compulsory public schooling is tantamount to state indoctrination in atheism.

In the context of this social controversy over evolution and religion, many science educators and advocates discourage public discourse—such as Dawkins'—that emphasizes putative conflicts between science and religion. Such confrontational language, they maintain, is likely to increase the suspicion and alienation of religious citizens, ultimately hindering efforts to improve public understanding of science in general and evolution in particular. An alternative view, defended by prominent scientists such as Kenneth Miller of Brown University, and maintained as official doctrine by many religious communities, is that contemporary evolutionary science is logically and empirically compatible with the existence of a supernatural creator. One widely held attempt to embrace both evolution and a creator god is called theistic evolution, according to which the creator god's intentions were in some way realized in the workings of natural selection and the other natural, law-like, causal processes that brought about the evolution of life. Over one third of the professional scientists in the U.S. accept some form of theistic evolution.[4]

Something like this view figured in a recent noted court case on the teaching of Creationism in American public schools. In *Kitzmiller et al. v. Dover Area School District et al.*, the U.S. District Court for the Middle District of Pennsylvania struck down a public school board policy that promoted "Intelligent Design," a form of Creationism. Kenneth Miller was called by the plaintiffs to offer his expert testimony—as a professional biologist who is also a Christian—against Intelligent Design. Judge John E. Jones III, in his December 2005 opinion, commented on the Creationist contention that evolutionary theory is incompatible with supernatural theism:

Their presupposition is that evolutionary theory is antithetical to a belief in the existence of a supreme being and to religion in general. Repeatedly in this trial, Plaintiffs' scientific experts testified that the theory of evolution represents good science, is overwhelmingly accepted by the scientific community, and that it in no way conflicts with, nor does it deny, the existence of a divine creator.

The Dover decision was almost universally applauded by scientists, science educators, and commentators, and seen by many as confirmation of the strategic wisdom of emphasizing the consonance of science and religion in public debates about evolution and evolution education. For their part, public intellectuals such as Dawkins, who wish to address science-religion conflicts, will sometimes respond to such conciliatory rhetoric by pointing out that it can be misleading or even intellectually dishonest.

I have a name for the broad thesis that there exist important conflicts between science and religion: I call it *agonism*. Those who accept agonism—and also wish to publicly discuss such conflicts—are *agonists*. The view that there exist no important conflicts between science and religion I call *accommodationism*. Those who either recognize no conflicts between religion and science, or who recognize such conflicts but are disinclined to discuss them publicly, I call *accommodationists*. In this paper I examine the debate between agonists and accommodationists in the context of the evolution-Creationism controversy in the United States, using Dawkins' recent work as a case study.

I begin by identifying a number of different claims that tend to be conflated in this debate. The first distinction is between a strategic or practical critique of agonism and other sorts of critiques. The strategic critique is that agonism is not helpful in attempts to ensure excellent science education in the relatively near term. This must be distinguished from the claim that agonism is not helpful in increasing the public appreciation of science in the long term. Second, when it comes to the strategic value of agonism to ensuring excellent science education in the near term, the following two claims must be disambiguated:

1. As a communication strategy for influencing public opinion and policy, agonism is less effective than accommodationism in ensuring excellent evolution education in a highly religious society.

2. The mere presence of agonism in public discourse is detrimental to attempts to ensure excellent evolution education.

In what follows, I argue that there is presently no compelling evidence for (1). While (1) is predicted by general considerations drawn from psychology, sociology, political science, and opinion research, more study on this specific empirical claim is required. However, I observe that the truth of (1) would not constitute evidence for (2). It may be the case that agonistic arguments fail as a strategy to persuade the relevant segments of the public that they should support evolution and oppose Creationism, but not the case that the mere presence of agonistic arguments in public discourse makes other such strategies less likely to succeed. In fact, there are plausible pre-theoretical grounds for thinking that the presence of agonistic perspectives in a public sphere that also includes accommodationist strategies actually makes the accommodationist strategies more effective.

What's Wrong with Accommodationism?

Agonists often claim that the conflict model is better supported by the evidence and more philosophically coherent. There are, of course, many ways that religion could conflict with science. One family of possible conflicts is *epistemological*, in which some piece of scientific knowledge provides reason—either by logical implication or evidentiary weight—to reject some piece of religious or theological knowledge (or to reject the piece of scientific knowledge). Another family of possible conflicts is *psychological*. The idea here is that the lives of individual scientists who uphold traditional religious beliefs and practices are characterized by more confusion, intellectual tension, unresolved contradictions, self-deception, or "compartmental thinking" than would be the case were they to lack traditional religious beliefs and practices. A life that unites science and religion suffers from psychological inconsistencies, it might be claimed.

Sometimes accommodationists attack the conflict model as a matter of psychology, by asserting that many professional scientists are devout religious believers. They note, for instance, that at least a third of U.S. scientists accept some form of theistic evolution. Agonistic commentators can point out that the overall distribution seems to suggest that at least among Americans, the practice of traditional faith does tend to be corroded by the practice of science, and biology in particular. In a survey of members of the National Academy of Sciences in the U.S.,[5] only 7% expressed "personal belief" in "a God in intellectual and affective communication with humankind." Biological scientists had the lowest rate of belief in a personal deity (5.5%) and immortality of the soul (7.1%). Compared with similar surveys by Leuba in 1913 and 1933, the rates of belief in a God and immortality among top scientists have declined significantly over the course of the 20th century. Some of the world's most prominent public intellectual-scientists have rejected traditional religious belief: Albert Einstein, Richard Feynman, Carl Sagan, James Watson, Francis Crick, Steven Weinberg, Murray Gell-Mann, Andrei Sakharov, Richard Dawkins, E.O. Wilson, Stephen

Jay Gould, Steven Pinker, Donald Johanson, Richard Leakey, and others. Darwin himself was unable to reconcile his Christian heritage with the understanding of nature that he helped develop. Describing himself in later years as an agnostic, Darwin wrote in his *Autobiography*[6] that no benevolent and sovereign creator could be responsible for the evolutionary process, "for what advantage can there be in the suffering of millions of the lower animals throughout almost endless time."

On the other hand, agonists can point out that conflict in the epistemological sense is compatible with concord in the psychological sense. A person can be inattentive to, or unaware of, epistemological conflicts among his beliefs; he may purposefully defer to a later date the resolution of conflicts he recognizes; or he may simply accept a high level of "cognitive dissonance." Dennett[7] explores how someone might continue to profess religious beliefs publicly even though he does not understand, or is uncommitted to, the contents of those beliefs. In a religious society, there are various social and moral incentives to profess belief, even when one does not, in fact, believe. For all of these reasons, when accommodationists point to cases of psychological concord, agonists may remain unmoved. Agonists can acknowledge cases of psychological concord but insist that these cases leave untouched what they regard as the more interesting and important relationships: namely, the epistemological. (The general point—that psychological and epistemological conflicts can be decoupled—is one that accommodationists could use insofar as they want to claim that agonists experience conflict between science and religion despite the absence of any actual conflict: an instance of the psychological without the epistemological.)

Similarly, when accommodationists claim that science by its very nature can neither affirm nor deny anything supernatural (the kind of accommodationism expressed by a National Academy of Sciences[8] document: "The statements of science invoke only natural things and processes"), agonists can respond by pointing out that this restriction of the domain of science does not prevent epistemological conflicts with religion from arising. For instance: if it is true, and known by theology, that God created humans; and if it is true, and known by science, that humans are mildly polygamous primates; then it follows logically that God created mildly polygamous primates. The statement *God created mildly polygamous primates* is no less theological in character than the statement *God created humans*. Indeed, it may carry theological freight that *God created humans* does not. Certainly, the statement invokes a supernatural thing. Nevertheless, it is a theological statement that one has a scientific reason to adopt (relative to a background belief that God created humans). This is so despite the fact that *humans are mildly polygamous primates* invokes only natural things and processes.

Another way to put the point is that scientific knowledge can have theological implications (epistemologically speaking) even if scientific knowledge neither affirms nor denies anything supernatural.

To take a somewhat more controversial example, Grunbaum[9] argues that the theological doctrine of continuous creation (which posits that all contingent energy would cease to exist if God's sustaining power were removed) is logically incompatible with the physical doctrine of conservation of energy. Generally, when agonists speak of (epistemological) conflicts between science and religion, they mean that certain features of our world as disclosed by science are better explained by supposing that they are the products of non-rational causal forces, rather than the work of a supernatural agent. In this sense, scientific knowledge can provide evidence against theism, on their view. This is so regardless of whether science can or cannot invoke the supernatural, and despite the peaceful psychological coexistence of religious belief and scientific practice in the lives of many.

What's Wrong with Agonism?

Reviewing *The God Delusion* for *Nature*, Krauss[10] reports that he was

> struck at how Dawkins' presentation, particularly in the early chapters where he builds his case against God, might offend those who, like myself, are quite sympathetic to his central thesis. I suspect that few thinking people of faith are unaware of the remarkable evil that has been done in the name of God, or the possibility that, although most cultures worship some god, this could be a mere reflection of the workings of the human brain rather than definitive evidence for God's reality. . . . At the very least I find it doubtful that constantly questioning the intelligence of "true believers" will be helpful in inducing any such reader to accept Dawkins' strongly argued thesis that both God and religion are nonsensical and harmful.

Krauss questions whether Dawkins' confrontational stance will be effective in winning converts to atheism or irreligion. Krauss places his critical remarks in the context of the evolution-Creation controversy:

> I wish that Dawkins, who has a gift for making science—in particular, evolutionary biology—both exciting and understandable to a broad audience, had continued to play to his strengths, which are desperately needed now more than ever as we confront growing attacks on the teaching of evolution, not just in the United States but in the UK and Europe.

It is understandable that Krauss chooses this social context as the setting for his review, as Dawkins is perhaps the most prominent authority on evolutionary biology in the world. But of course the question of how best to win converts to atheism or irreligion is not identical to the question of how to bolster evolution teaching.

In fact, Dawkins is quite explicit that the principal goal of his book is not to persuade people to endorse evolution teaching, or to (de)convert the devout, but rather to "raise the consciousness" of atheists, agnostics, and those questioning their faith. In the preface, he writes:

> I suspect—well, I know—that there are lots of people out there who have been brought up in some religion or other, are unhappy in it, or are worried about the evils that are done in the name of religion; people who feel vague yearnings to leave their religion and wish they could, but just don't realize that leaving is an option. If you are one of them, this book is for you. It is intended to raise consciousness: raise consciousness to the fact that to be an atheist is a realistic aspiration. You can be an atheist who is happy, balanced, moral, and intellectually fulfilled.

Given this overriding aim, one cannot criticize the effectiveness of Dawkins' project by pointing out that it alienates potential allies in the evolution-Creation struggle, or even that it alienates ardent religious believers. Despite these alleged effects, his project nonetheless might be successful at raising the consciousness of skeptics. One could question the greater moral or social importance of this goal, but that would be a much different sort of critique.

One of the means by which Dawkins attempts to raise consciousness in his book is by insisting that religion be subject to the same intellectual, moral, and conversational standards as all serious claims in our public life. No claim ought to be impervious to criticism simply by virtue of its source in faith or religious tradition. Dawkins, along with many secular rationalists, hopes that his efforts are contributing to a long-term project of cultural reform in which religion will eventually wither away and Enlightenment values—chief among them the acceptance of science as the authority on metaphysical matters—will gain near-universal acceptance. It is perfectly plausible that such a cultural reform, if it is to be possible at all, will necessitate a thoroughgoing critique of religion. At the least, the question of the effectiveness of agonism in the long-term project of (neo-)Enlightenment cultural reform is distinct from the question of the effectiveness of agonism in the relatively near-term project of ensuring excellent science education. It could be that agonism is unhelpful in influencing the curriculum decisions and the quality of science teaching in the immediate future, but also indispensable to bringing about a society in which there is little-to-no religiously motivated resistance to evolution.

Given this, one might be tempted to think that the choice between an agonistic stance or an accommodationist stance could be made by weighing the relative values of improving science education in the near term versus achieving a more enlightened public in the long term. However, in a free and open society characterized by rich pluralism of intellectual perspectives and institutions, science advocates are not forced to choose between agonism and accommodationism. Both perspectives can coexist and find space in the marketplace of ideas. Agonists and accommodationists could criticize each other on empirical or philosophical grounds, but the strategic, prudential argument would be misplaced insofar as the two stances are intended to accomplish different social aims.

We need to be clear about the complaint that Krauss and others are lodging against the agonist. It could be the complaint that as a communication strategy for influencing public opinion and policy (in a highly religious society—i.e., one in which a majority of adults attend religious services regularly), agonism is less effective than accommodationism in ensuring excellent evolution education. Call this claim weak accommodationism. It follows from this that science educators *qua* science educators should be more accommodating. However, this claim is open to the pluralist response sketched above; namely, that some science educators may adopt accommodationist strategies even as other scientists engage in more agonistic discourse in public. So long as there are sufficient numbers of able, accommodationist science educators at work, agonistic scientists like Dawkins may feel justified in dismissing the charge that they are misallocating their talents by pursuing the long-term cultural project. This accommodationism is weak in the sense that agonists could grant it without giving up their central position.

Is there a stronger version of the accommodationist complaint that could foreclose this avenue of response by the agonist? The stronger version is that the mere presence of agonism in public discourse is detrimental to attempts to ensure excellent evolution education. Thus, it is not enough to appeal to an intellectual division of labor in which the near-term educational work is given to the relatively more accommodationist. According to this stronger thesis, agonists are endangering the educational work of accommodationists by refusing to join in their stance.

I now wish to argue that while this stronger thesis is not implausible, there is no evidence for it. Furthermore, I will argue that it is no less plausible that the presence of agonism in public discourse is actually on balance *beneficial* to accommodationist educational outreach.

Miller and Pennock: Holding the Center

Miller and Pennock[11] situate their discussion of public attitudes about science and religion against the backdrop of the recent history of religiously motivated interference in science teaching in America. While a majority of Americans support science and technology and believe it has improved their lives,

> there are strongly held religious views that conflict with modern science. Moreover, these latter views have become amplified in recent decades with the political ascendancy of Christian fundamentalists within American politics, who seek to insert their views into science classes and establish them as the norm. There is also a sizable group of people in the middle whose general support for science may be vulnerable in particular areas.

Miller and Pennock maintain that there is a soft middle of the American public that holds moderate views on science and religion, but whose opinion could be swayed in the direction of religious conservatives. Therefore, the "question for American science education in the 21st century is whether the center will hold in the face of pressure from the religious conservatives." While Miller and Pennock do not explicitly defend the strong accommodationist thesis that the presence of agonism in public discourse is detrimental to attempts to ensure excellent evolution education, the findings they present and interpret might be construed as support for this thesis.

To characterize the ideological center on science and religion, Miller and Pennock present a fine-grained analysis of polling data over 20 years (1985-2005) that has measured American adults' degree of agreement with the statements, "science and technology have made our lives healthier, easier, and more comfortable" and "we depend too much on science and not enough on faith." About the support for the first statement, Miller and Pennock conclude that there is a "substantial plurality of American adults who believe that science and technology make their lives healthier, easier, and more comfortable and that only about 6% of adults in the U.S. disagree strongly with this idea." On balance, they say, "these data show that there is broad public acceptance of the idea that science and technology have improved the quality of our lives, but that a majority of adults are only moderately committed to this proposition."

About the support for the statement, "we depend too much on science and not enough on faith," Miller and Pennock conclude that "although the proportion of strongly held views on this statement has increased over the last 20 years, a substantial majority of Americans hold much more moderate attitudes on this issue." In support, they observe that only about 20% of American adults have strong convictions on the subject, with roughly 10% completely agreeing with the statement and 10% completely disagreeing. Americans who express a high level of agreement with the statement number 29%, while 21% express a comparable level of disagreement. This means that the remaining 50% of American adults "hold a mixed or uncertain attitude about the conflict between scientific and religious ideas."

Miller and Pennock consider this group to represent "swing votes" in the evolution-Creation debate, and they offer a series of concrete proposals designed to prevent the loss of swing votes "to missionary Creationists." Among these proposals, which include a discussion of college-level science requirements and informal science education outside of the schools and universities, they assert: "we need to do a better job explaining what real science is and what it is not. Students need to know how science is different from faith and limits itself to testable hypotheses. They need to know why science may not appeal to supernatural explanations and why it is neutral with regard to metaphysical religious beliefs." So, Miller and Pennock can be read as advancing the accommodationist position as part of a strategy to influence the moderate middle to favor evolution teaching and oppose the teaching of Creationism.

One limitation to Miller and Pennock's analysis is that it leaves unclear exactly what the moderate middle believes. Miller and Pennock seem to treat American adults' attitudes toward the statement "we depend too much on science and not enough on faith"[12] as a measure of their attitudes on "the conflict between religious and scientific ideas." But why should we assume that when a person expresses uncertainty or mixed views about society's reliance on science over religion, that person also holds mixed or uncertain views about the conflict between scientific and religious ideas? Clearly, as a matter of logic, the claim that we depend too much on science and not enough on faith does not commit one to any particular position on the conflict of religious and scientific ideas. A person could think that religion and science have non-overlapping domains but worry that the scientific domain receives too much attention relative to the religious domain. Or a person could think that religion and science offer up incompatible ideas, while remaining unsure about how much we should depend on any of them.

Suppose that we could establish more firmly that roughly half of American adults hold a "mixed or uncertain attitude about the conflict between scientific and religious ideas." The portrait of the moderate middle is still left impressionistic because we do not know what this mixed attitude amounts to. One possible mix of attitudes combines a belief that science and religion are consonant in some areas of knowledge (plant biology, for instance) but not in others (human origins, say). As Miller and Pennock remind us, Americans' scientific knowledge is a patchwork of sometimes incongruous beliefs. In 2005, only 6% rejected the claim that over periods of millions of years, some species of plants and animals adjust and survive while other species die and become extinct; but 39% rejected the claim that human beings, as we know them today, developed from earlier species of animals. It is entirely consistent with the available polling data that the aggregate of people with "mixed" attitudes on the religion-science conflicts might have relatively conservative views in specific areas, such as human evolution versus special creation. In that case, an accommodationist message on theistic evolution, for example, may not be significantly more appealing to the "moderate" middle than to the "fundamentalist" fringe.

I think it is fair to say that if the construct of the moderate middle is to be useful in adjudicating between agonist and accommodationist strategies on evolution, the data adduced by Miller and Pennock would have to be supplemented in order to develop a clearer picture of this segment of the public.

The lack of a detailed portrait of the moderate middle limits our ability to draw conclusions about the best strategic science communication on evolution and creation. For all we know, agonism may in no way influence the middle against the teaching of evolution; it might even be helpful. In the final section of this article I present a hypothesis to that effect. Before doing so, it will be illuminating to look at another line of research and public commentary, which takes aim more directly at agonism.

Nisbet and Mooney: Accommodating "Frames"

Nisbet and Mooney[13] suggest that Dawkins is aiding the cause of Creationist activists:

> If the defenders of evolution wanted to give their creationist adversaries a boost, it's hard to see how they could do better than Richard Dawkins, the famed Oxford scientist who had a bestseller with "The God Delusion." Dawkins, who rose to fame with his lucid expositions of evolution in such books as "The Selfish Gene," has never gone easy on religion. But recently he has ramped up his atheist message, further mixing his defense of evolution with his attack on belief.

The problem with Dawkins' approach, according to Nisbet and Mooney, is that:

> The public cannot be expected to differentiate between his advocacy of evolution and his atheism. More than 80 percent of Americans believe in God, after all, and many fear that teaching evolution in our schools could undermine the belief system they consider the foundation of morality. Dawkins not only reinforces and validates such fears—baseless though they may be—but lends them an exclamation point.

Public support for the teaching of evolution could be weakened not just by acerbic Oxford professors, we are told, but by anyone who argues that science and religion are in conflict:

> The Dawkins-inspired "science vs. religion" way of viewing things alienates those with strong religious convictions. Do scientists really have to portray their knowledge as a threat to the public's beliefs? Can't science and religion just get along? A "science and religion coexistence" message conveyed by church leaders or by scientists who have reconciled the two in their own lives might convince even many devout Christians that evolution is no real threat to faith.

Elsewhere,[14] Nisbet and Mooney recommend to scientists and other science communicators a theory of "framing" that could assist them in persuading the public on science-related policy questions. In their terms, frames "organize central ideas, defining a controversy to resonate with core values and assumptions. Frames pare down complex issues by giving some aspects greater emphasis. They allow citizens to rapidly identify why an issue matters, who might be responsible, and what should be done." In this understanding, a frame is what would otherwise be known as an argument or reason, but with special attention paid to appealing to core values and assumptions rather than challenging them.

Nisbet and Mooney could be making the relatively weak, pluralist claim above: namely, that as a communication strategy for influencing public opinion and policy (in an overwhelmingly religious society), agonism is less effective than accommodationism in ensuring excellent evolution education. While this claim is surely intuitive, and is predicted by general considerations from psychology, communication theory, opinion research, and political science, there is to date no empirical literature dedicated to it.[15] For example, such general considerations suggest that when people perceive that some of their core beliefs and values are threatened by some new source of information, they tend to react by closing themselves off to that information source, rather than reasoning through its intellectual implications in a dispassionate manner with the aim of arriving at a more consistent set of commitments.

Nisbet and Mooney also appear to be committed to the stronger accommodationist claim, as when they suggest (above) that the success of *The God Delusion* not only fails to help resist Creationism in the schools, but actually aids Creationism. However, they do not offer any evidence for this stronger claim. They do cite the success of a 2004 media campaign in California that swayed opinion among the voting public, and was sufficient to pass a $3 billion ballot initiative on stem cell research funding, despite the religiously motivated opposition surrounding this sensitive, beginning-of-life issue. The campaign made use of "frames" such as "social progress" and "economic competitiveness." Similarly, Nisbet and Mooney suggest that public sympathy for the Creationist cause in public schools will be best countered by "frames of 'public accountability' that focus on the misuse of tax dollars, 'economic development' that highlight the negative repercussions for communities embroiled in evolution battles, and 'social progress' that define evolution as a building block for medical advances...." Again, there is to date no empirical research into these predictions specifically.

It is worth noting that even if Nisbet and Mooney's recommended communications strategy in the evolution-Creation controversy were entirely sound, it would not constitute evidence for strong accommodationism. For if, as they contend, the arguments of social progress, economic development, and public accountability promise to be the most successful, we might expect them to succeed even in the context of a broader marketplace of ideas in which one can also find arguments about the philosophical conflict between evolution and Creationism. The case of the California stem cell campaign could be interpreted as an example of a something quite like this. Debates in American public life over stem cell research have included a plurality of perspectives, many of them overtly antagonistic to religion.[16] One of the most vocal early supporters of public funding for stem cell research was Ronald Reagan, Jr., a publicly avowed atheist who directly challenged the theological objections of its opponents.[17] Despite the presence of these perspectives in the broader marketplace of ideas, the California campaign appears to have worked.

Even by their own description of their work, Nisbet and Mooney are not presenting an empirical theory of science-religion accommodationism, or any particular device for "framing" science policy debates. Instead, they are pointing out the general failure of scientists to produce and consult empirical research on public communication when determining how to communicate with the public in such debates. At the same time, they are advocating a particular research program that should shed light on the kind of strong accommodationism they entertain.

The Dawkins Effect

Having considered some possible detrimental effects of agonist discourse on science education, we should consider a possible beneficial effect. In the present media environment, conflict is an adaptive trait. Narratives of conflict attract media attention and can heighten general public interest in material that might otherwise be perceived as too stolid or academic. No doubt the combative tone of Dawkins' *The God Delusion* and the resulting media attention in part explain its sales of over 1.5 million copies worldwide, an extraordinary feat for a book that is essentially an application of science and philosophy to theological matters. It may be that many of Dawkins' readers belong to his target audience of those who were already skeptical of traditional religion and spirituality. Nevertheless, the public debate about the book and its implications spilled over into mainstream media markets. Dawkins was seen on Fox News and on the cover the *Time* magazine, for example.

The *Time* magazine coverage took the form of an extended dialogue between Dawkins and Dr. Francis Collins, a scientist who directs the National Human Genome Research Institute and is also an outspoken Christian.[18] The article, "God vs. Science," was accompanied by images of a wizened Charles Darwin apparently about to engage in a wrestling match with an angel. In the course of the discussion, Collins has ample opportunity to testify to the psychological and epistemological compatibility of science and religion. Given the instinct of mass media producers to provide "balance" by presenting equal coverage of two (or rarely more than three) sides between which the viewer is invited to choose, the use of the religion-science conflict narrative has the effect of creating a platform for the opposing position. In this case, the opposing position was not anti-scientific religion—which admits conflict and simply favors the victory of religion over science—but instead the position I have been calling accommodationism. On the other hand, when the "balanced" view includes anti-scientific religion, and agonism is presented as the opposing end of that ideological spectrum, then accommodationism naturally emerges as the reasonable compromise position.

I do not mean to endorse any of these claims. What I wish to suggest is that they are pre-theoretically plausible scenarios for the effects of agonist discourse in a pluralistic marketplace of ideas that also includes accommodationist discourse, and that they enjoy no more and no less empirical support than the strong accommodationist claim that the prominent discussion of science-religion conflict is detrimental to strategic efforts to ensure excellent science education in America.

In light of this, it would be interesting to investigate the following hypothesis, which might be labeled *The Dawkins Effect*:

The Dawkins Effect: The presence of messages of science-religion conflict makes messages of science-religion harmony better known and more palatable to religious believers.

The idea is that the discussion of science-religion conflict in mass media-driven public discourse results in greater public awareness of messages of science-religion harmony. The Dawkins Effect has a corollary: it also makes the harmony messages seem like a reasonable compromise between anti-scientific religion and anti-religious atheism. In short, the presence of overtly agonist scientists such as Dawkins may make accommodationist scientists like Collins appear more reasonable to religious believers, and may make the prospect of adopting accommodationist views as a basis for public policy seem more judicious and fair to the moderate middle.

Another effect of agonistic discourse might be to galvanize self-identifying secular supporters of science who might otherwise not become involved in public policy debates. Such people might indeed be mobilized to combat the perceived common threat posed by the Creationist movement. At work in many discussions of agonism, accommodationism, and evolution education, such as those above, is the assumption that achieving broad public consensus on evolution and creation is important to securing sound science teaching in public schools. At the same time, most observers agree that the Creationist movement, like so many effective movements of social change, is the work of a relatively small, well-organized, highly motivated minority. While it may be ideal in a democracy for a piece of education policy to have the support of a stable majority, a consensus is often not necessary to achieving the success of the policy. After all, the present public school policy of excluding Creationism from science curricula in the United States does not enjoy broad public support among the American people. Most Americans would prefer to see both views taught.[19] In light of this, agonists could argue that conflict literature such as *The God Delusion* may indeed benefit evolution education by mobilizing science supporters to become politically engaged with this issue, and this apart from any potential alienation it might cause among the religious segments of the public who remain politically disengaged on this issue. Unfortunately, neither this nor (as I hope to have shown above) any of the accommodationists' alternative hypotheses, can claim compelling evidentiary support.

Conclusion

The critical reception of Richard Dawkins' *The God Delusion* and related works sheds light on the debate over how best to communicate evolutionary science to the public, and how best to secure high-quality evolution teaching in public schools in such highly religious societies as the United States. It is useful to analyze the debate as a disagreement between agonists and accommodationists. Agonists assert that there exist important conflicts between science and religion and they wish publicly to discuss such conflicts. Accommodationists are those who either recognize no conflicts between religion and science, or who recognize such conflicts but are disinclined to discuss them publicly. The question is whether agonism helps or harms efforts to ensure excellent evolution education. Here it is important to distinguish the question of the effectiveness of agonism in a long-term project of (neo-)Enlightenment cultural reform from the question of its effectiveness in the relatively near-term project of influencing science teaching and education policy.

With respect to the latter question, one criticism of Dawkins' confrontational approach is that it is likely to alienate religious believers who are potential allies against the Creationist agenda. This could mean either the relatively weak thesis that as a communication strategy for influencing public opinion and policy, agonism is less effective than accommodationism at promoting good evolution education, or the strong thesis that the mere presence of agonism in public discourse is detrimental to evolution education. The weak accommodationist thesis is plausible, and predicted by general considerations from psychology and social science research. However, there is no evidence for it presently available. I surveyed arguments by Miller and Pennock, Nisbet and Mooney, and concluded that they do not provide evidence for the stronger accommodationist thesis. Surely this is an important research program. At the same time, it would be useful to explore the Dawkins Effect; namely, the hypothesis that the presence of messages of science-religion conflict makes messages of science-religion harmony better known and more palatable to religious believers.

Endnotes

1. M. Shermer, *Rational Atheism: An Open Letter to Messrs. Dawkins, Dennett, Harris and Hitchens*, http://www.sciam.com/article.cfm?id=423C1809-E7F2-99DF-384721C9252B924A&page=1, November 21, 2007.

2. *Gallup,* "Third of Americans say Evidence has Supported Darwin's Evolution Theory: Almost Half of Americans Believe God Created Humans 10,000 Years Ago," November 19, 2004.

3. The Pew Forum on Religion and Public Life, "Public Divided on Origins of Life," August 30, 2005.

4.   This number comes from a random survey of 1,000 persons listed in the 1995 *American Men and Women of Science* conducted in 1997 by Larry Witham and Edward J. Larson. Forty % of respondents agreed with the statement, "Man evolved over millions of years from less developed forms of life, but God guided the process, including the creation of man." See L. Witham, "Many scientists see God's hand in evolution," *Washington Times* (April 11, 1997), A8. Reprinted online at http://www.ncseweb.org/resources/rncse_content/vol17/5319_many_scientists_see_god39s__12_30_1899.asp (accessed February 24, 2088).

5.   E.J. Larson and L. Witham, "Leading Scientists still Reject God," *Nature* 394 (1998): 313.

6.   C. Darwin, *The Autobiography of Charles Darwin, 1809-1882* (New York: W. W. Norton & Company, 1993), 90.

7.   D. Dennet, *Breaking the Spell: Religion as a Natural Phenomenon* (New York: Viking, 2006).

8.   D. Kennedy *et al.*, National Academy of Sciences, 1998.

9.   A. Grünbaum, "Theological Misinterpetations of Current Physical Cosmology," *Philo* 1, 1 (1998).

10. L. M. Krauss, review of *The God Delusion, Nature* 443, 26 (October 2006).

11. Miller and Pennock, present volume.

12. Perhaps in conjunction with the statement "science and technology have made our lives healthier, easier, and more comfortable" as well.

13. M. Nisbet and C. Mooney, "Thanks for the Facts. Now Sell Them," *Washington Post*, April 15, 2007.

14. *Nisbet & Mooney, "Framing Science," Science* 316, no. 5821 (April 6, 2007): 56.

15. Nisbet, personal communication, 2007.

16. Harris, 2004.

17. Ronald Reagan, Jr., Letter to the Editor, *New York Times*, August 12, 2004.

18. David Van Biema, "God vs. Science," *Time,* November 5, 2006.

19. The Pew Forum on Religion and Public Life, "Public Divided on Origins of Life," August 30, 2005.

4. The Cultural Particularity of Conflict between "Religion" and "Science" in a Global Context

Frank L. Pasquale

"Science" and "religion" are foundational concepts in Western thought. They are widely spoken of, and conceived of, as monolithic and adversarial phenomena. They are both, however, in the words of anthropologist Beatrice Whiting, incredibly complex "packaged variables." As such, they are meaningful generalizations, but also misleading and sometimes counterproductive ones, rather than homogeneous realities. They are particularly counterproductive in the form, "religion *versus* science." Upon close scrutiny it becomes apparent that—depending upon the definitions of "religion(s)" or "the sciences" being employed—there is no necessary or wholesale conflict between something called "religion" and something called "science." There are, rather, particular "religious" ideas and ideologies of time, place, and culture that have conflicted with particular facts, findings, or theories emerging from the natural sciences on particular subjects.

Few literate people, if any, reject the laws of thermodynamics, the periodic table of the elements, or the concept of gravity on religious or any other grounds. And even with regard to biological and human evolution, if we step back from the nearly obsessive preoccupation with this topic in the United States, only a minority of literate people worldwide exhibit whole-cloth philosophical or "religious" rejection of it.[1]

The very habit of speaking *as though* there is necessary and wholesale conflict between "science" and "religion" is problematic. "Religion"-"science" adversarialism, conceived and broadcast as established fact, makes for sensational headlines and high-energy crossfire on cable television programs. But it does little to advance human understanding or to promote *reasonable* plural co-existence informed by substantial appreciation for scientific learning. Moreover, it may well erode the global competitiveness of societies that devote substantial attention and resources to such preoccupations.

In what follows, several tendencies among the most ardent partisans of a purported wholesale battle between "science" and "religion" are challenged:

- overgeneralization and over-simplification on both sides of this argument.

- failure to recognize and acknowledge the *particularity* of "conflicts" between "science" and "religion."

- a noticeable tendency among some "science" partisans to view "religion" as a monolithic threat to all rational or scientific thought, and for some "religious"partisans to view "science" and some of its most important findings as significant threats to any and all forms of "religious faith" and to the moral health of society.

Implications of the purported dispute between "science" and "religion" for scientific, technological, and economic competitiveness will also be considered.

Historical Particularity

The concepts of "religion" and "science" emerged within the Western intellectual tradition. They have been viewed in many quarters as intimately related, yet antagonistic, phenomena. A standard cavalcade of celebrated flashpoints is habitually cited, among them conflicts between Roman Catholic orthodoxy and Copernicus or Galileo Galilei; scriptural literalist rejection of "Darwinism" and the evolutionary descent of man; and religious obstacles to empirical medicine. Bertrand Russell, in *Religion and Science,*[2] does a customarily lucid job of recounting these and other examples of orthodox suppression of natural discoveries in biology, geology, physics, anatomy, physiology, and the practice of medicine.

This duly noted, however, another Russell (historian of science Colin A.) has observed that the "conflict thesis…obscures the rich diversity of ideas in both science and religion" and "ignores many documented examples of science and religion operating in close alliance."

> Neither of these has ever been monolithic, and there was seldom a unified reaction from either. Thus, in the case of Galileo, it was the Roman Catholic, not the Protestant, wing of Christianity that appeared to be at odds with science. In the Darwinian controversy, a uniform response was lacking even within one branch of Protestantism…. Moreover, the scientific community was deeply divided over religion

in Victorian England, the mathematical physicists being far more sympathetic than the scientific naturalists. The conflict thesis fails to recognize such variety.[3]

Upon close consideration of the historical record, there is ample reason to question the assumption or assertion of necessary and wholesale religion-science conflict, even within a Christian context. Moreover, it becomes fairly clear that the natural sciences as we now know them may well have never emerged without certain ideas that grew out of the Christian intellectual tradition.

Alfred North Whitehead,[4] for example, observed that the distinctive character of Christian theism in Europe played a critical role in the emergence of an equally distinctive focus on the systematic discovery of rational principles underlying nature. It was, he suggested, the concept of a personified, rational, and *universal* God (particularly by the time of the Middle Ages) that laid the foundation for the "scientific" conviction that behind the welter of seemingly disparate natural events lay unifying principles that were universal and discoverable through reason and empirical method. This did not happen, for example, in China, despite much earlier emergence of technological achievements far in advance of Europe, as amply documented by Joseph Needham.[5] As Shigeru Nakayama notes:

> The Platonic conviction that eternal patterns underlie the flux of nature is so central to the Western tradition that it might seem that no science is possible without it....[A]lthough Chinese science assumed that regularities were there for the finding they believed that the ultimate texture of reality was too subtle to be fully measured or comprehended by empirical investigation. The Japanese paid even less attention to the general while showing an even keener curiosity about the particular and the evanescent.[6]

A sharply drawn distinction between "natural" and "supernatural" forces, processes, or phenomena was a consequential development in human thought, particularly as developed in the West. There is no similar distinction observable in preliterate cultural worldviews, nor is it any more likely to have been made by prehistoric humans. Rather, extrapolating from what we do know of preliterate cultures, there was an indistinguishable interplay of what we now view as "natural" and "supernatural," or "empirical" and "magical," in early attempts to predict, control, and come to grips with the nature of physical reality.

A gradual teasing apart of natural and magical or supernatural conceptions has been a transformative development in human history. James Thrower[7] documents the roots of an "alternative [naturalistic] tradition" in surviving texts from the ancient world, including Greece, Rome, China, and India, among others. But it was within the Christian intellectual context, building upon Platonic notions of an ideal nether-realm, that a particularly well-defined distinction between *deorum* (things of God or a transcendent realm) and *saeculorum* (things of this world or "of Caesar") emerged most pointedly. This created an intellectual (secular) "space," as it were, within which the very conception of scientific or empirical inquiry, as we now know it, coalesced.

Coherently and self-consciously secular, naturalistic, or scientific ways of thinking emerged in Europe out of, and in reaction to, Christian orthodoxy—tentatively in the Middle Ages, building force and focus in the Renaissance, and quite assertively by the time of the Age of Enlightenment.[8]

> Religion, in the history of European "progress," moves away from magical thinking and opens the door for rationalism....[A]mong medieval scholars...human reason was placed alongside divine revelation as a way of knowing truth. This interest in the potential of human reason to understand things in conjunction with divinely-revealed knowledge cleared a space for reason to function independently over the succeeding centuries. The separation of natural from supernatural, and reason from revelation, allowed thinkers to focus on the human study of natural phenomena.[9]

But this did not, until more recently in certain quarters, require an *absolute* separation of "religious" from "scientific" among practitioners of empirical inquiry. Rather, it was the very conviction of a divine plan underlying the physical laws of nature that motivated practitioners of emerging empirical inquiry, from Bacon to Newton to Kelvin. The notion that something called "religion" and something called "science" were in necessary, wholesale, and unavoidable conflict, or that one must choose between a "religious" *or* a (thoroughly naturalistic or non-transcendental) "scientific" worldview, is a later development. Colin Russell places this in the "Victorian scientific naturalism" of the late 19th century.

> In its simplest form this was a concerted attempt to replace conventional religion (which deals with the supernatural) by a world-view that involves nature and nature only. Its aim was the secularization of society....[10]

It was at this point, Russell suggests, that "what has variously been called a 'military metaphor' or the 'conflict thesis' came into being." It was galvanized, or perhaps prompted, by the wholesale rejection of "Darwinism" by some, but by no means all, representatives of Christian churches in Victorian England. It is, as Russell characterizes it, an "enduring mythology." But it is hardly universal. It is largely a product and preoccupation of Western intellectual history that has been taken up more intensely in the United States, for cultural reasons peculiar to it, than in most of the remaining economically developed world (including—ironically—present-day Britain).

Cultural Particularity

One will be hard-pressed to find a parallel *adversarial* distinction between "religion" and "science" in most of Asia. On the one hand, the very notion of "religion" has never comfortably fit Asian schools of social, philosophical, and metaphysical thought. The difficulty with which "Buddhist," "Confucian," "Daoist," or "Hindu" worldviews and related behavior are shoehorned into the European concept of "religion" is well known. On the other hand, the various sciences—together with mathematics, engineering, and technology—tend more to be treated as an array of practical tools for achieving desirable personal and societal ends. The distinctive character and preoccupations of Asian religio-philosophical schools of thought do not generally present the natural sciences with the kinds of full-frontal conceptual or ideological assaults presented by selected monotheistic adherents.

If anything, much of Asian thought, particularly in everyday life, has been characterized by a blurry admixture of naturalistic and meta-empirical thinking. Challenges to science education, practice, and literacy tend to be, paraphrasing Sun Yat Sen's phrase, a tray of loose folk beliefs—magical, "superstitious," or "pseudo-scientific." Much like the sand in Sun's original metaphor, this may present an erosive grit to the workings of scientific inquiry or education, but not a coherent system of thought in wholesale opposition to the sciences in general. As Helaine Selin observed in the *Encyclopaedia of the History of Science, Technology, and Medicine in Non-Western Cultures*, the notion of "science as a distinct rationality valued above magic is uniquely European. It is not common to most non-Western societies, where magic and science and religion can easily coexist, even today."[11]

In China, despite early emergence of an impressive array of advanced practical technological achievements, famously documented by Joseph Needham, "science" was neither conceptualized nor pursued with the systematic coherence seen in Europe. The "Chinese had sciences, but not 'science,' not a single conception or word for the sum of all scientific divisions."[12] In an attempt to explain this, anthropologist Francis Hsu stressed a characteristically practical, task-specific, and human-centered turn of mind that exhibited comparatively "little interest in the unseen or the imaginative" *or* universal theorizing.

> The matter-of-fact attitude toward the supernatural makes it almost inevitable that the Chinese should fail to define the natural world in terms of atoms, gravitation, parabolas, and geologic strata, all of which are extremely remote from that which is open to the senses and experience.[13]

Due, in part, to a decidedly this-worldly tone and focus in much of Chinese philosophy (exemplified by that of Kongfuzi or "Confucius," the Daoists, Xunzi, and Wang Chong, among others), a sharply defined contrast and conflict between "natural" or "secular" (on one hand) and "supernatural" or "divine" (on the other) never emerged as it did in the Christian context. Rather, indistinct references to "heaven" or the "Dao" paid vague homage to the mysteries of fate, human life, the universe, or the fundamental incomprehensibility of existence itself. Upon reflection on such matters, Asian philosophers habitually lapsed into poetry and metaphor rather than attempts to construct detailed rational arguments. And beneath the arc of heaven, animistic or spiritualistic folk beliefs (and related ritual practices) were often seamlessly woven into everyday life. So they remain in many of these cultures today.

Buddhist, Confucian, Daoist, "Hindu," and other Asian religio-philosophical traditions present little coherent basis for the kind of wholesale rejection of scientific "attitude," inquiry, or conclusions seen in the West. There is little, if any, *philosophical* basis for rejection of evolutionary theory, for example. And what *mythological* bases there may be, tend to be regarded more metaphorically than ontologically. "In traditional Chinese thought," writes Christoph Koerbs, "ideas about the origin of the world do not involve any concept of creation by an almighty creator but only by impersonal processes of spontaneous self-creation."[14] Rather than conflicting with evolutionary theory, such worldviews provide broad contexts within which the mechanism of evolutionary process may be placed with little conceptual difficulty. To this point, Barbara Sproul notes that:

> The Buddha was essentially uninterested in the question of the origin of the universe, declaring "Inconceivable, O Monks, is this Samsara [wheel of rebirth]; not to be discovered is any first beginnings of beings." Further, he rejected any idea of a personal creator god, claiming that the world goes through successive periods of expansion and contraction, unaffected by the activities of the gods.[15]

In the Indian subcontinent, Susantha Goonatilake observes that in contrast to convulsive reactions among many in Europe to Copernicus or Darwin,

> [n]one of these events would have had the same impact on South Asia, whose cosmology allowed for a large number of worlds, for evolution and change, for humans as part of a larger living world, and for a subconscious.[16]

Goonatilake also notes that "ancient South Asian ideas on fundamental issues had several parallels with those in modern science," including the considerable age of the universe, compatible doctrines concerning the nature of material reality, "a multiplicity of valid truths," and the notion that "the world that presents itself to the senses is not the most real."[17]

In Japan, the "New Learning" in the 19th century (of ideas and technologies from the West) did not include the adoption of a religion-versus-science posture. Western scientific knowledge and technological methods were readily recognized and embraced as an array of useful tools. Buddhist, Confucian, and native Shinto worldviews did not—separately or in concert—present an overarching conception of reality at odds with methodological naturalism in the conduct or interpretation of the empirical sciences, or beliefs about organic or human origins that prevented acceptance of biological (including human) evolution. It is no surprise that, as reported by Miller and Pennock[18] elsewhere in this volume, Japan ranks among the nations most accepting of evolutionary theory (with 78 percent of adults describing evolution as "true").

This does not mean, of course, that all members of these cultures are immune to the intuitive appeal of human evolutionary exceptionalism or to "Western-style" (including Islamic) fundamentalist religious condemnation of evolutionary theory, particularly where education or access to evidence for evolution is limited. So, for example, the slickly packaged, intuitively appealing, and competent sounding philippics of Turkish evolutionary critic Adnan Oktar (written under the pseudonym "Harun Yahya")[19] may penetrate the philosophical insulation afforded by Asian worldviews and confuse or convert some—particularly the less well-educated—at least for the present. But the key point is that in much of Asia, lack of education, folk beliefs, and "common sense" intuition may present challenges to scientific education and practice, but not, in general, coherent philosophical opposition rooted in traditional worldviews or sacred texts. *That*, like the notion of "science" itself, is a Western invention espoused, exported, and imported by some.

Religious and Cultural Particularity Concerning Bio-genetic Science and Technology

The cultural contrast becomes quite apparent—and significant, from a policy perspective—with regard to bio-ethical positions on genetic and biological research, such as cloning or therapeutic embryonic stem cell research. Unlike some adamantly "faith-based" positions taken against such techniques in the West, most notably in the United States, Jens Schlieter concludes that

> Buddhists seem to have taken a fairly neutral attitude to cloning. It seems that, provided no harm is done to any of the beings involved, the procedure of cloning as such does not offend religious feelings or basic value sets in Buddhism. This is evidenced by the rather relaxed way in which therapeutic and reproductive cloning are discussed by South and South-East Asian Buddhists.[20]

The long-range consequences of these new bio-technological powers—desirable, undesirable, and the cost-benefit balance between them—are not known. As a result, human beings seek ethical guidance from many quarters, including religio-philosophical traditions. It is fascinating to observe how prominent cultural figures from many quarters (scientific, philosophical, religious, commercial, and governmental) draw from traditional cultural materials as one source of values to frame, anchor, and guide ethical debate and decision-making about such matters. This process is often tentative and sometimes messy, but quite understandable. In the absence of definitive long-range consequential data, sound judgment and prudent decision-making are fraught with uncertainty.

Since those whose teachings shaped the traditional worldviews and moral/ ethical texture of these cultures could not have foreseen the novel choices now before us, extrapolation from general value principles embedded in cultural tradition or foundational texts is unavoidable. So it is that while some interpret Buddhist proscriptions on killing to extend to the human fetus from the moment of conception,[21] most do not. And regardless of influential voices representing particular interpretations of what "Buddhist principles" and texts may have to say about such matters, popular opinion and behavior in most Asian countries indicates pragmatic, if cautious, acceptance. In the absence of strong, unequivocal doctrines embedded in (or interpretively extracted from) traditional religio-philosophical teachings, the economic and therapeutic benefits of such technologies generally wins the day in China, Japan, Singapore, Thailand, India, and even South Korea, despite its substantial Christian population. For example, Horres, Ölschleger, and Steineck note that:

In Japan, biomedical research is seen as a key factor for the future development of the economy as well as social welfare....The issue of human cloning is a show case in this respect. An analysis of public opinion, governmental decision making, and bioethical reasoning indicates different attitudes in these spheres of discourse. Public opinion is generally favorable and focuses on the medical benefits promised by reproductive medicine. The government's attitude is additionally shaped by the international viability of such research. Expert opinions vary greatly, with the strongest opposition to cloning and the destruction of human embryos coming from bioethicists with a background in the humanities. However, their arguments have so far been virtually ignored by the public, the government, and scientists working in the field.[22]

And elsewhere, Renzong Qiu observes:

The Chinese belief is that human life begins with birth, not the instant when the sperm penetrates the ovum; thus a human embryo or fetus has not become a person yet, although they should enjoy certain respect, such as that afforded a corpse....Thus, embryo research or deriving stem cells from an embryo *per se* are not ethically problematic.[23]

From a Confucian perspective, the critical question is when the human organism becomes a "person" (by internalizing culture and becoming a *social* or "relational" being). This process begins at birth. As Cynthia Fox notes in her account of "the global race to capture and control the stem cell,"[24] those "nations that [view] the start of human life as a 'process, not a moment'" have had more favorable attitudes toward therapeutic cloning. Asian cultures have generally tended toward this view.

But, then, we need not move so far afield to find such contrasts with the particular religious objections that have recently held sway in American policy. With respect to the matter of therapeutic use of embryonic stem cells, as Eric Cohen notes, "the preeminent Reform, Conservative, and Orthodox Jewish organizations in America have all given their ethical endorsement, seeing embryonic stem cell research as not only permissible under Jewish law but an embodiment of Jewish values."[25] Cohen, in fact, is one of several vocal dissenters who sees a deeper and "more universalistic wisdom" in the Roman Catholic condemnation of what it views as "instrumental" treatment of organisms that, based on long but variable orthodoxy,[26] are inviolably human from the moment of conception.

It is not the purpose here to evaluate the merits or limitations of any of these positions. These are matters of great consequence, and they require careful and thoughtful consideration from many vantages. The point being made here is simply that the notion that "religion" is a monolithic obstacle to the conduct, teaching, learning, or valid interpretation of scientific inquiry—or related technological exploration—is, quite simply, an untenable and counterproductive simplification. This has been true through history, across cultures, and even among thinkers, denominations, and sects within monotheistic, and specifically Christian, contexts.

"Science" and "Religion" as Symbolic Threats

Why, despite ample historical and cultural evidence of the particularity of "science-religion" conflict, is the notion of monolithic opposition so irresistible, at least in certain quarters? This seems attributable, in large measure, to *some* partisans on either side who wish to "convert" others to substantially naturalistic *or* transcendental worldviews, and to some who—while they may not aim for wholesale conversion—fear perceived threats to their own worldviews and ways of life symbolized by the "opposition."[27]

Some who present themselves as "science" advocates fear that even the slightest trace of meta-empirical or metaphysical commitment renders doing, comprehending, or accepting scientific inquiry impossible. This rests on a faulty assumption and assertion that nothing less than *thoroughgoing* philosophical (or "atheistic") naturalism is a necessary prerequisite for doing and understanding "science." On the other side, some advocates of (particular forms of) "religion" fear "science" as a dangerous temptation or slippery slope to a thoroughgoing naturalism that undermines any and all metaphysical or transcendental anchors for human understanding and, more importantly, for morality. Neither fear is (necessarily) true, but it is notable that partisans in each camp exhibit a pronounced tendency to frame these matters in either-or, with-me-or-against-me terms.

At the heart of the matter, of course, lies the fact that the natural sciences restrict their attention to "material" or "physical" processes and their properties, while religions (as commonly defined) allow or affirm meta-empirical or supernatural entities and events. This said, it is manifestly not necessary for people doing or interpreting science effectively to restrict their worldviews *entirely* to a materialist or physicalist (or "atheist") outlook. An *essential* degree of materialist "buy-in" is required, but not *thoroughgoing* materialism, physicalism, or naturalism. There are ultimate, metaphysical questions about which the natural sciences can say little or nothing. And there exists a range of metaphysical ideas that are not obstacles or enemies to natural scientific inquiry or findings. So it is that Francis Collins[28] and Kenneth Miller[29] embrace *particular versions* or interpretations of monotheistic religiosity and teach science, or unreservedly embrace evolution and repudiate fellow religionists (of particular types) for rejecting it on theological or scriptural grounds.

What is Essential for Effective Scientific Literacy, Education, and Practice?

Elsewhere in this volume, William Cobern[30] introduces a distinction between "methodological" and "philosophical" *secularism* as part of a general strategy for effective science education. Offering the example of theist and atheist scientists who collaborate with one another in the laboratory without conflict, he suggests "methodological secularism"—or the subordination, but not categorical exclusion, of metaphysical beliefs—as an effective conceptual and pedagogical platform for teaching, learning, and doing science. This involves the application of canons and methods of the empirical sciences to inquiry about *anything*—including, if students so wish, religiously inspired ideas. Thoroughgoing commitment to, or "belief" in, ("atheistic") philosophical naturalism is not a prerequisite for doing, or teaching and learning, the natural sciences.

As Robert Pennock noted during ISSSC's Workshop on Science Education and Secular Values, however, "mere" methodological naturalism (or secularism) may not be sufficient.[31] A substantial degree of commitment to ontological naturalism is necessary, for example, to warrant certification of material scientists and engineers involved in designing and building bridges. At some level, "belief in" the naturalistic perspective underlying pertinent scientific principles and procedures is necessary. But it may be asked, "belief in" what, precisely? With respect to the engineering and building of bridges, acceptance of the laws of gravitation, the periodic table of elements, and the calculable properties of metals and other construction materials is surely critical. Momentary recourse, while calculating material stresses, to a magical or miraculous belief in anti-gravitational suspension in spans being erected at a conjunction of "spirit lines" would no doubt have dire consequences.

On the other hand, it is hardly necessary for material scientists or bridge engineers to accept a comprehensively skeptical, agnostic, or "atheist" stance toward *all* metaphysical ideas or possibilities. Some of these lie well outside the scope of empirical inquiry, such as notions of "ultimate meaning" or purpose of human (or all of) existence, the origins or eternity or "ultimate nature" of all that exists, or even *samsara, karma,* or a non-interventionist, Deistic, teleological, or personal "God." Each of these can be defined and embraced in ways that present no direct or substantial threat to the acceptance of scientific methods or findings, including evolution or what it takes to design and build good bridges.

Some call this "compartmentalization," but this may be a mischaracterization. Many who hold such ideas often view them as *integral* to their conception of existence and to the natural processes elucidated by the sciences. A conviction that somehow all that exists is inexorably advancing toward a coherent denouement of some kind, or that there is some transcendent coherence or "intelligence" underlying the welter of everything we perceive, need not conflict with any feature of the natural world and its properties as described or explained by the natural sciences (including evolution). To the contrary, for some, this enriches it.

As one of the Connecticut high school students who responded to ISSSC's call for essays on science education[32] wrote:

> Science is what adds beauty to our universe and makes everything so much more amazing....Personally I find the view science gives us of the universe as intriguing as I do because I love my God, the creator of this universe, and with each new thing I learn, some of God's glory is revealed to me....Although I could never completely understand how every single aspect works together, I am now somewhat familiar with the intense complexity of all things, and therefore I am reminded of our glorious creator and wanting to learn more. Although this reason alone is more than enough to keep me interested in science, I also realize that there are many individuals just as enthralled about the subject who don't share my faith....

Whether intended or not, this writer, in a deft piece of irony, seems to turn the tables on thoroughgoing naturalists—suggesting that *even* those who hold a thoroughly materialist or physicalist worldview *may* be able to appreciate the profound wonder of the natural world revealed by the sciences, as do those who view this as "God's handiwork."

Some metaphysical, meta-empirical, or "religious" ideas are clearly anathema to empirical scientific methods, evidence, interpretation, and progress. Some (concerning questions and speculations that truly transcend the scope of the natural sciences) are not.[33] Whether it is better, in the long run, for human beings to dispense with all "faith" commitments to metaphysical ideas for which there is no, or insufficient, empirical evidence is a worthy debate—in philosophy and theology. But this debate has substantially less relevance or utility in discussions of the appropriate content and conduct of science education or practice. With respect to the latter, it is more pertinent to distinguish as clearly as possible between those domains that can effectively be addressed and explained by the natural sciences and those that cannot. It is more productive to ascertain how much and what kinds of naturalistic buy-in are essential for (credential-worthy) scientific learning and practice. It is not necessary to expunge *all* metaphysical speculation or transcendental commitments in order to maintain a substantial, effective, or certifiable commitment to empirical inquiry or the proper understanding of its methods and findings.

The distinction between "methodological" and "philosophical" naturalism (or secularism) is valuable, but these particular adjectives may themselves be problematic. "Methodological" suggests to some a delimited or provisional posture of "going along" with certain procedures, methods, or conceptual prerequisites for doing science or engineering without real commitment to their necessity or validity. It requires only that practitioners or interpreters of science operate *as though* the world works in accordance with discoverable natural principles, even if there is not substantial conviction that this is ontologically (or "really") true. But this is not quite the point, and such a posture may, indeed, not be sufficient. Pennock is right to question whether *this* is really enough to ensure that scientists and engineers can be certified to do science and engineering appropriately, effectively, validly, and dependably.[34]

It may be clearer to speak of *essential* and *thoroughgoing* naturalism. *Essential naturalism* denotes the scope or degree of substantive commitment to non-transcendental, non-supernatural, non-magical, materialistic, or naturalistic thinking necessary for valid conduct, interpretation, teaching, and learning in particular scientific fields. *Thoroughgoing naturalism* refers to an insistence that *all* traces of metaphysical, meta-empirical, transcendental, or supernatural thinking be expunged. The latter is manifestly not necessary to learn or "do science" and to learn or do "it" well. An effective "scientific attitude" requires essential, not thoroughgoing, naturalism.

Surveying the historical and cultural evidence, it becomes apparent that although "science"[35] has been and continues to be challenged wholesale by selected religious individuals and minorities, the greater long-range threats are sheer lack of education and the more pervasive challenge of "magical" thinking (which persists even among those who have access to education in substantially science-literate societies).

The larger question is: how much, or what forms of, "magical" or otherwise mistaken causal thinking must be surrendered in order to effectively learn, do, and interpret empirical (and perhaps more importantly, medical) science? It is quite likely that this question would occupy center stage in a workshop on scientific, medical, or technological education and practice in East or South Asia, rather than the challenges to geological or evolutionary theory presented by minorities of "scriptural literalists" or religious apologists in some places. In view of a noticeable growth in "pagan," pantheistic, "New Age," and "spiritualistic" orientations in the United States, this larger question may, over time, eclipse the very particular challenges of "Creationism" or "Intelligent Design" to evolution and increasingly take center stage in such workshops here, as well.

Meanwhile, we will do well to be circumspect about references to "science" and "religion," monolithically conceived, and any purported general relationship or wholesale conflict between them. Wider recognition and acknowledgement of the particularity—in time, place, and topic—of ideological conflicts between some thoroughgoing naturalists and some "religious fundamentalists," or between specific religious tenets and specific empirical understandings of the natural world, should help in the effort to persuade a majority of minds of the value and validity of empirical inquiry. And it should help to marginalize extreme partisans—and their arguments—on either side of purported "religion-science" conflict.

Implications for Global Competitiveness

From a broad historical and global perspective, the notion of wholesale science-religion conflict looks like an exceptional and dysfunctional cultural preoccupation, particularly as it plays out in the United States. Among the major developed and emerging industrial nations, wholesale symbolic denigration of "science" or rejection of biological and human evolution is nowhere more acute than here. The degree to which other developed and developing industrial nations do not suffer from this ideological donnybrook, as we continue to, is the degree to which our competitive position in the world may well erode.

In his treatise on the reasons societies falter and collapse, Jared Diamond[36] observes that it is sometimes a society's most defining and deeply held ideas and values that, when held too tenaciously in the face of changing conditions, become the seeds of its decline or failure. The distinction between divine and temporal realms, so central in Western thought, has been, in many respects, a uniquely productive one. But, like any human principle, it can become destructive as well. It gave birth to experimental method and the systematic discovery of nature's universal laws. But it also gave rise to a philosophical dispute whose benefits, if any, are difficult to discern. As Diamond counsels, we must gain sufficient perspective to distinguish which ways of thinking and valuing are worth holding onto, and which are not.

The heated and highly publicized dispute between absolutist partisans of "science" and "religion" has the regrettable side-effect of confusing, alienating, or polarizing a generally thoughtful, if tentative, majority[37] that may have limited comprehension of scientific methods or findings, but would otherwise be receptive to education and sensible attitude formation based on sound evidence—presented moderately. As a result, the "religion-science" dispute cannot help but act as a drag on scientific and technological education, practice, and innovation. It diverts public attention from more productive concerns, saps energy and resources, and undermines the societal resolve necessary to maintain our competitiveness in science education and practice. This polarization becomes particularly problematic at a time when other major developed and developing nations do not exhibit the same corrosive ideological disputes.

With the rise of East and South Asian economic, industrial, and technological prowess, the religion-science conflict thesis would seem to be a myopic cultural preoccupation that can ill be afforded. Students from these regions assiduously absorb the best that European and American education can offer in the sciences, mathematics, and technology. Many gratefully take what they learn back to their rapidly growing home cultures, where scientific and technological pursuits enjoy increasing public and policy support, comparatively unhampered by "scriptural literalist" challenges. Indeed, as Cynthia Fox notes, even some scientists in the West are finding opportunities in Asia irresistible, such as genetic research laboratories stocked with cutting-edge technology and freshly trained young researchers in Singapore, sans "faith-based" policy hurdles and ideological constraints faced at home.[38]

What is the way out of our culturally constructed and counterproductive war between "science" and "religion"? It would seem to be, as in many such situations, that disputants on both sides must set aside some of their claims and fears. We must achieve a fundamental shift in our cultural assumptions and worldview. Metaphysical combatants behind both thoroughgoing naturalistic and theologically fundamentalist battle lines must surrender their respective absolutist convictions and hegemonic hopes. If there is a lesson to be learned from Asia in this regard, it is that there are some aspects of existence that elude our powers of rational comprehension. Some of these will likely always elude us. It is perhaps better to lapse into poetry about these, rather than being presumptuously certain or categorically dismissive about them, while we get on with the practical business of discovering whatever we can about nature that will help improve the human condition and satisfy our indomitable desire to understand—to the extent that our precious yet limited tools enable us to do so.

ENDNOTES

1. See country data on acceptance or rejection of evolution presented by Jon D. Miller and Robert T. Pennock in Chapter 1, p.21.

2. Bertrand Russell, *Religion and Science* (Oxford, UK: Oxford University Press, 1961).

3. Colin A. Russell, "The Conflict of Science and Religion," in Gary B. Ferngren, ed., *Science and Religion: A Historical Introduction* (Baltimore: Johns Hopkins University Press, 2002), 9.

4. Alfred North Whitehead, "The Origins of Modern Science," in *Science and the Modern World* (New York: Macmillan, 1925), Chapter 1. Reprinted in Alfred I. Tauber, ed., *Science and the Quest for Reality* (New York: New York University Press, 1997), 53-69.

5. Joseph Needham and Wang Ling, *Science and Civilisation in China* (Cambridge: Cambridge University Press, 1954-2004).

6. Shigeru Nakayama, "Japanese Science," in Helaine Selin, ed., *Encyclopedia of the History of Science, Technology, and Medicine in non-Western Cultures* (Dordrecht: Kluwer Adademic Publishers, 1997), 465.

7. *The Alternative Tradition: Religion and the Rejection of Religion in the Ancient World* (The Hague, Netherlands: Mouton, 1980).

8. See, for example, James Thrower's *Western Atheism: A Short History* (Amherst, NY: Prometheus Books, 2000).

9. Karen Louise Jolly, "Magic and Science," in *Encyclopedia of the History of Science, Technology, and Medicine in non-Western Cultures,* 524.

10. Colin A. Russell, *Cross-currents: Interactions between Science and Faith.* (Grand Rapids, MI: William B. Eerdmans, 1985), 193.

11. "Introduction," in *Encyclopedia of the History of Science, Technology, and Medicine in non-Western Cultures,* xv.

12. Christoph Koerbs, "East and West: China in the Transmission of Knowledge from East to West," in *Encyclopedia of the History of Science, Technology, and Medicine in non-Western Cultures,* 262.

13. Francis L. K. Hsu, *Americans and Chinese: Passages to Differences,* 3rd ed. (Hawaii: University of Hawaii Press, 1981), 386.

14. Christoph Koerbs, Op cit., 265.

15. Barbara C. Sproul, *Primal Myths: Creating the World* (New York: Harper & Row), 194.

16. Susantha Goonatilake, "East and West: India in the Transmission of Knowledge from East to West," in *Encyclopedia of the History of Science, Technology, and Medicine in non-Western Cultures,* 268.

17. Ibid., 268.

18. See Chapter 1.

19. See Cornelia Dean, "Islamic Creationist and a Book Sent Round the World," *The New York Times*, July 17, 2007. (http://www.nytimes.com/2007/07/17/science/17book.html?ref=science). See also Harun Yahya's website: http://www.hyahya.org/.

20. Jens Schlieter, "Some Observations on Buddhist Thoughts on Human Cloning," in Heiner Roetz, ed., *Cross-cultural Issues in Bioethics: The Example of Human Cloning (At the Interface//Probing the Boundaries 27)* (Amsterdam: Rodopi, 2006), 179.

21. See, for example, William B. Hurlbut, "Science, Religion, and the Politics of Stem Cells," *Social Research*, 70 (3) (Fall 2006): 810-834; R. E. Florida, "Buddhist Approaches to Abortion," *Asian Philosophy*, 1 (1) (1991): 39-50 (http://ccbs.ntu.edu.tw/FULLTEXT/JR-ADM/florida.htm).

22. Robert Horres, Hans Dieter Ölschleger, and Christian Steineck, "Cloning in Japan: Public Opinion, Expert Counselling, and Bioethical Reasoning," in Heiner Roetz, ed., *Cross-cultural Issues in Bioethics: The example of Human Cloning (At the Interface/Probing the Boundaries 27)*, 17.

23. Renzong Qiu, "Bioethics: A Search for Moral Diversity," *Eastern Mediterranean Health Journal*, 12 (Supplement 1) (2006): 321-329.

24. Cynthia Fox, *Cell of Cells: The Global Race to Capture and Control the Stem Cell*. (New York: W.W. Norton & Company, 2007).

25. Eric Cohen, "A Jewish-Catholic Bioethics?" *First Things*, 154 (June/July 2005), 7-10.

26. See, for example, David Albert Jones, "The Appeal to the Christian Tradition in the Debate about Embryonic Stem Cell Research," *Islam and Christian-Muslim Relations*, 16 (3) (2005): 265-283.

27. Alternatively, it reflects a battle between those who strive for a thoroughly "religionless" world or a theocratic one. "Science" and selected scientific findings (such as evolution) regrettably become weapons in this battle for hegemony.

28. Francis S. Collins, *The Language of God: A Scientist Presents Evidence for Belief* (New York: Free Press, 2006).

29. Kenneth R. Miller, *Finding Darwin's God: A Scientific Search for Common Ground between God and Evolution* (New York: Harper Perennial, 2000).

30. See Cobern, Chapter 5.

31. Trinity College, Hartford, CT, May 22, 2007.

32. See a full summary of the student essays by Ariela Keysar and Frank L. Pasquale elsewhere in this volume.

33. See, for example, Ian G. Barbour, *When Science Meets Religion: Enemies, Strangers, or Partners?* (San Francisco, CA: Harper San Francisco, 2000).

34. Point made during ISSSC's Workshop on Science Education and Secular Values, Trinity College, Hartford, CT, May 22, 2007.

35. … in particular times and places, with regard to particular issues.

36. Jared Diamond, *Collapse: How Societies Choose to Fail or Succeed* (London: Penguin Books, 2005).

37. This is the "center" worth "holding," as described by Miller and Pennock in Chapter 1.

38. Fox, *Cell of Cells: The Global Race to Capture and Control the Stem Cell.*

Teaching Science

5. The Competing Influence of Secularism and Religion on Science Education in a Secular Society

William Cobern

> Give to Caesar what is Caesar's, and to God what is God's.
>
> *Jesus of Nazareth*

> It is simply no use trying to *see through* first principles...If you see through everything, then everything is transparent. But a wholly transparent world is an invisible world. To *see through* all things is the same as not to see.
>
> *C. S. Lewis*

The United States is a country in which, according to the Constitution, there can be no religious test for public office. On the other hand, we have a Bill of Rights that guarantees the free exercise of religion. We call this a secular system of government, and sometimes go so far as to use Jefferson's phrase that there is a "wall of separation" between church and state. For the most part, this secular system of government comports well with the Christian teachings based on Jesus' remark that one should render unto Caesar that which belongs to Caesar, and unto God that which belongs to God.

John Richard Neuhaus once remarked that ours is a *naked* public square—naked, that is, with regard to religious ideas or commitments. The reality, however, is that the public square abhors a philosophical vacuum, and thus the public square of our so-called secular society has never really been completely disrobed. Until the mid 20th century, for better or for worse, the philosophy permeating the public square was loosely that of Protestant Christianity, especially in the institutions of public education. That effectively ended with a

Supreme Court decision in the early 1960s banning prayer in schools. I suppose that after this decision, many people thought we had arrived where we should have been all along: that is, at a truly naked public square. But I suggest that the public square really does abhor a philosophical vacuum, and that today we often find secularism competing with various religious ideas for prominence. When it comes to science education in the public schools, I suggest that what we need is a different understanding of secularism, if we are to avoid one round of conflict after another.

Religion in Public Life

Jesus of Nazareth, on whom Christianity is based, commands his followers: Give to Caesar what is Caesar's, and to God what is God's. Separation of church and state would seem a natural outgrowth of such a command. Indeed, Christian churches since the colonial period have strongly embraced the perspective made explicit in the Bill of Rights:

> Congress shall make no law respecting an establishment of religion, or prohibiting the free exercise thereof....

Given the diversity of Christian churches, and their (for the most part) shared belief that faith is a matter of voluntary acceptance, non-establishment of religion was the key to free exercise of religion, and it remains so.

Those who reject any notion of the transcendent have always been happy to join Christians[1] in their embrace of the first amendment to the Constitution. For non-believers, non-establishment meant that as modernization proceeded, so would the spread of secularism. According to the twin theory of modernization/secularization, secularization is the expected culmination of modernizing forces: urbanization, rationalization, professionalization, functional differentiation, and bureaucratization;[2] and coincident with secularization is the asymptotic decay of traditional religion, which, without fully disappearing, is nonetheless relegated to the private spheres of personal life. Well, perhaps so in Europe;[3] but not in the USA, where belief in God holds steady, even among many scientists.[4] According to The Barna Group in 2006:

- 71% believe in God when God is described as the all-powerful, all-knowing, perfect creator of the universe who rules the world today.

- 7% believe that God is the total realization of personal human potential.[5]

George Gallup, who has polled Americans about their belief in God since the 1940s, has come to the conclusion that "so many people[6] in this country say they believe in the basic concept of God, that it almost seems unnecessary to conduct surveys on the question."[7] Indeed, rather than non-establishment being the key to secularization, it has been key to religious vitality in the U.S., most noticeably for Protestant Christianity but also for Catholicism, and other religions as well.

Protestant Christianity has been so vital that non-establishment came to mean a *de facto* establishment of, indeed, a vague ethos or philosophy of Protestant Christianity, especially for the institutions of public education.

> For most of American history, a Protestant cultural hegemony dominated American public life, especially the cultural climate of the public schools. Evangelical prayers, Bible devotionals, the Common Sense philosophy, conservative admonitions to shun the common vices (justified by Scriptural proof-texts), the evangelical ethos of proselytizing with one's personal witness, the piety of the born-again, traditional gender roles: these features constituted much of the fabric of normative American values. Religious minorities—Catholics, Mormons, Amish, Jews, Jehovah's Witnesses, and others—typically conceded the mainstream culture to Protestants and withdrew into religious subcultures. It is not hard to see why many Protestants sincerely believed that America was an intrinsically Protestant nation.[8]

Indeed, Protestant cultural hegemony during the 19th and early 20th centuries meant anti-Catholic bigotry in American politics. This bigotry led most states to pass "Blaine Amendments"—state constitutional provisions prohibiting the use of state revenues for the support of sectarian schools (where "sectarian" was a thinly veiled reference to Catholic schools).[9] The façade of non-establishment—which was nonetheless an establishment of Protestant Christianity in the public square—could not last forever, however; its obvious inconsistencies, coupled with the forces of social and cultural change, were its undoing. As Bob Dylan sang in the 1960s: the times they are a'changing. In the late 1950s, American views toward sexual morality began moving away from traditional Christian morality. There were the Kinsey Institute reports, which made sex a normal part of the public discourse. *Playboy* appeared on newsstands everywhere, followed by a host of other such sexually explicit magazines. The impact of the sexual revolution, sparked by the birth control pill, cannot be understated; as a result, sex education in the public schools became a forgone conclusion. Constitutional law was changing; U.S. Supreme Court decisions in the 1930s, 1940s, and 1950s used the Non-Establishment clause of the First

Figure 5-1
American Beliefs [10]

What do you believe about the origins of human beings?[11]		Do you personally believe in the existence of God?[12]	
51%	God created humans in present form.	92%	Believe
30%	Humans evolved, God guided the process.	5%	Don't believe
15%	Humans evolved, God did not guide process.	3%	Not sure
These percentages are quite constant across numerous polls and various ways of asking these two questions.			

Amendment to disestablish Protestant hegemony. *Engel v. Vitale* (1962) and *Abington v. Schempp* (1963) ended legal school sponsorship of prayer and Bible devotionals. And court-ordered busing for school desegregation in the late 1960s severely weakened the local control of schools.[13]

In contrast, issues pertaining to the teaching of science, particularly evolution, remained relatively quiescent during this otherwise turbulent period through the 1970s. The 1925 Scopes trial created considerable angst over the teaching of evolution in public schools, but in the wake of that trial, evolution largely disappeared from school curricula for the next 25 to 30 years. Renewed interest in science education and evolution finally erupted in the wake of the 1959 Darwin Centennial celebration,[14] where it was declared that 100 years without Darwin were enough. The Biological Sciences Curriculum Study (BSCS), which was funded by the National Science Foundation, soon made evolution a key feature of its innovative high school biology textbook series, which ended the Darwinism curriculum draught. The response—Scientific Creationism—came almost immediately. Hyper-conservative Christians began to promote Young-earth Creationism in the public schools—an effort that was brilliantly documented by Ronald Numbers in *The Creationists*; and of course this Creationist response precipitated yet another round of non-establishment litigation during the 1980s.[15]

Is there an end in sight? It did not come in the 1990s, when challenges to the teaching of evolution took a new form: Intelligent Design. These challenges also failed in the courts;[16] and yet polling suggests that, whatever accommodations Christians may have come to regarding morality, culture, politics, and schooling, belief in God and the rejection of evolution remain strong in the United States (see *Figure 5-1*).

Moreover, religious interests in recent years have been asserted in other science-related areas such as cloning, embryonic stem cell research, and climate change. That we are in the early years of the 21st century and secularism *still* has yet to drive religion from the public square (weakened though it may be) has the likes of Richard Dawkins, Daniel Dennett, and Sam Harris in the throes of apoplexy.[17] Their recent books—*The God Delusion*; *Breaking the Spell: Religion as a Natural Phenomenon*; and *Letter to a Christian Nation*, respectively—which have all appeared on the *New York Times* best seller lists, amount to hysterical pleadings for driving out, once and for all, the religious barbarians from the rightful place of secular intellectuals (or "Brights," as Dennett calls them).[18]

So, *is* there an end in sight? Is there a way forward? There is, but it does not lie with a Dawkins/Dennett/Harris call to arms for a final victory in the American cultural wars. In public education, and with specific reference to science education, we need to embrace a differentiated understanding of secularism. Explaining what this might mean requires that we first re-examine what would seem to be a settled issue: the definition of religion.

Methodological and Philosophical Secularism

Religion is surely the belief in a deity or deities, whether defined by Christians, Jews, Muslims, Hindus or whomever. Accordingly, those who believe in no deity are not religious. This very popular line of thought is, however, quite antiquated, taken from a time when virtually everyone believed in some form of deity. So has religion simply disappeared for non-believers? Or, rather, has religion taken new forms? For these questions, C. S. Lewis is instructive: "It is simply no use trying to *see through* first principles...If you see through everything, then everything is transparent. But a wholly transparent world is an invisible world. To *see through* all things is the same as not to see."[19] Skeptics often claim to "see through" religious claims, but they err in thinking that there is anything at all beyond fundamental beliefs. We may think of it as a worldview;[20] everyone operates from a set of fundamental beliefs. For some, those beliefs involve a deity or deities, whereas for others there is only matter and energy. Dawkins, Dennett, and Harris are believers; they are just not theistic believers.

Despite the political advantages that a traditional definition of religion might accrue for some (this way some ideas are automatically excluded without having to argue the merits), we are more accurately served by following the lead of Paul Tillich: religion is ultimate concern.[21] We all have ultimate concerns; we all have first principles. These are the ways in which we answer the most fundamental questions of life. It is not that someone like Richard Dawkins is irreligious, but rather that traditional religions are not the source for the way he answers the religious questions of life, which he nevertheless answers. We are all religious, rejection of the transcendent notwithstanding; and for this reason the American public square will never be naked. Attempts to make it so should be seen for what they are: a grab for cultural hegemony.

As noted at the start of this essay, there is a religious—a Christian— embrace of secularism that can well serve the public. Secularism, however, takes different forms that are neither equally acceptable from a Christian perspective[22] nor equally efficacious with respect to peace in the public square. The forms are *methodological* secularism and *philosophical* secularism. These terms are an amalgam of ideas from Paul de Vries and Wilfred McClay. In a 1986 article on naturalism and natural science from a Christian perspective, de Vries addressed the difficulties that theists have with the "naturalism" of the natural sciences, given that naturalism typically requires the disavowal of *super*naturalism. De Vries' counterargument is that scientists do not actually practice naturalism in their work, in that everyday science is practiced regardless of any position on the supernatural. Theists and atheists coexist in the lab without problem or conflict. It was of no consequence in the physics community that Abdus Salam was a practicing Muslim or in the biology community that Francis Collins is a practicing Christian.[23] De Vries argues that such amiable comportment is possible because scientists implicitly practice *methodological* naturalism rather than *philosophical* naturalism, which indeed does disavow the supernatural. This would be pragmatism at its finest. After all, the reason we call it the *natural* sciences is that scientists seek explanations *in* nature, not elsewhere. In the words of Galileo, "the intention of the Holy Ghost is to teach us how one goes to heaven, not how heaven goes."[24] And, although from the time of Darwin to the present the Huxleys and the Dawkins of the scientific community have tirelessly argued that the *natural* of the natural sciences does indeed imply philosophical naturalism, there is no reason to allow this very shrill and very small minority view to drive public policy, especially given that their claim is so thoroughly rebutted by the factual descriptions of practicing scientists such as Collins and Salam.

Just as de Vries argues that there are two legitimate ways to look at naturalism, Wilfred McClay argues that there are two legitimate ways to look at secularism. His argument is drawn from an analogy to Isaiah Berlin's "Two Concepts of Liberty." Berlin distinguished between "negative liberty, which designates a freedom from external interference—a freedom to be left alone—and positive liberty, which means a freedom to be self-governing and self-directed."[25] Analogously, argues McClay, there is a difference between negative secularism and positive secularism. Secularism, he posits, can be understood as an opponent of established belief—including a nonreligious establishment—and a protector of the rights of free exercise and free association. Second, secularism can be understood as a proponent of established unbelief and a protector of strictly individual expressive rights. The former view, on the one hand, is a minimal, even "negative" understanding of secularism as a freedom "from" establishmentarian imposition. For this view, the secular idiom is merely a provisional lingua franca that serves to facilitate commerce among different kinds of belief, rather than establish some new "absolute" language, an Esperanto of post-religious truth.

The exact meaning of "positive" and "negative," as they modify "secularism," is not readily grasped. De Vries' use of "philosophical" and "methodological" is far more transparent. Bringing the two lines of argument together, it is sensible to distinguish between philosophical secularism and methodological secularism. Philosophical naturalism and philosophical secularism represent philosophies that are deeply antithetical to theism. In American culture, they are not going to be the "new 'absolute' language, an Esperanto of post-religious truth."

In contrast, methodological naturalism and methodological secularism are shorn of the presuppositions of anti-supernaturalism and promote the instrumental use of these concepts. This methodological, pragmatic, instrumental use of secularism as a public policy invites all parties to the public square. This is "a provisional lingua franca that serves to facilitate commerce among different kinds of belief." Such facilitation of people's differences strikes me as just what secular values (or my preferred term, democratic values) are all about, including: fairness, tolerance, respect for others, good citizenship, independent thought, and so forth. But I don't see these as the values of philosophical secularism.

In constitutional terms, non-establishment means there can be no religious test for public office or policy. Constitutional free exercise within a policy of methodological secularism, however, means that neither can a person's ideas be excluded from the public square on the grounds that they are religiously motivated. For instance, a person should not be excluded from, say, the public policy debates on funding embryonic stem cell research merely because that person's position was derived from Christian doctrine. By the same principle, an atheist shouldn't be excluded from the debate because his views are derived from philosophical naturalism. In other words, methodological secularism refers to the terms of engagement, or the rules of play, by which people confront each other civilly with their opposing ideas. What is required is that people incorporate the rules of play into whatever position, philosophy, or worldview they hold. Philosophical secularism is partisan; it is *one* team claiming to own the rules.

Four Rules for Teaching Science

Policy debate is one thing, however; school curricula are another matter. Can the openness of methodological secularism work as a policy for the public schools? Won't methodological secularism be interpreted as an open classroom door for Creationism, Intelligent Design, and whatever comes next? The answers are "yes"—methodological secularism can work effectively as policy for the public schools, and "yes"—there is a risk. The most worrisome, troublesome, persistent case of conflict is the scientific teaching of origins, but there are other areas of potential conflict, for example:

- Embryonic stem cell research
- Cloning
- Sustainability and environmentalism
- Animal rights
- Traditional knowledge (e.g., First Nations, Aboriginal, Native American)
- Climate change
- Dissection

But the teaching of origins clearly precipitates the most conflict in science education.[26]

Evolutionary theory is the scientifically accepted account for the natural development and speciation of life on earth. It also cannot be denied that the development and implementation of school curricula is a political process, subject to individual interpretation, and dependent on the good faith of those involved. The day-to-day decisions of each science teacher are enormously influential. America simply does not have a strong central curriculum with central testing to enforce the uniform implementation of a common policy. The public polices the implementation of curricula that it (i.e., the public) has chosen; and it does so via elected school boards. The formal efforts to either dilute the teaching of evolution or implement sectarian topics such as Creationism and Intelligent Design precipitate public challenges, all of which have been effective to date. But there is still the individual teacher, who is still quite autonomous; and there are still the students with questions that originate from many more places than just the prescribed curriculum.

The subject of origins is inherently metaphysical, and teachers and students understand this implicitly. Once the topic of origins is broached, most students cannot help asking themselves: Why is there *anything* rather than nothing? Why is everything the way it is, and not some other way? Students ask these questions, and similar ones. Ask an uninhibited group of students these questions and the range of discussion will stretch from material causes to spiritual causes. My point is that the topic of evolution almost always prompts people to think about "cosmic questions," which is a vernacular reference to metaphysics and religion. Consider the late Carl Sagan and his *Cosmos* TV series. Sagan's intention was for "cosmos" to be understood scientifically, since the program is about scientific cosmology. Picture, if you can, the opening scene. Picture what the viewing audience sees on TV: a pontificating Carl Sagan standing before an ethereal backdrop, "The cosmos, all there is, all there ever was, all there ever will be." Sagan undoubtedly thought he was speaking scientifically, but from these very first words, amplified by the mystery-laden backdrop from which he spoke, his program has deep metaphysical implications. It could hardly be otherwise, even without the visual theatrics.

Why? Because evolution offers a mechanism for how things have come to be as they are, and we—metaphysically—quite naturally wonder: Is evolution a *sufficient* mechanism for what we believe about our world? We wonder—metaphysically—if there isn't something *more* that is needed. We wonder—metaphysically—if what we otherwise believe about the world is *compatible* with ideas from evolution. The historian of science David Hull asks: "What kind of God can one infer from the sort of phenomena epitomized by the species on Darwin's Galapagos Islands?[27] He had in mind the answer Sagan and also physicist Steven Weinberg would give: no one with a reasonable understanding of biological science could believe in God—or at least in any God having anything to do with our natural world.[28] Then there is biologist Julian Huxley, who promoted himself as a kind of high priest for a "religion without revelation" based on a global evolutionary humanism.[29] A surprisingly different answer comes from David Lack. Textbook accounts of evolution typically refer to "Darwin's finches" as an important source of evidence for evolution. Actually, Lack did the study of finches in support of evolutionary theory. In contrast to Sagan, Hull, Huxley, and Weinberg—and I think it is fair to say that Lack met Weinberg's criteria of having "a reasonable understanding of biological science"—Lack tells us something very different:

> The true significance of the first chapter of Genesis is to assert that God made the universe and all in it, that He saw that it was good, and that He placed man in a special relationship to Himself.[30]

Clearly, Lack had no difficulties with Hull's question about God and evolution, nor would Francis Collins and many others. The issue of interest here is not one view or another, whether it is the view of a Sagan or a Collins, but, rather, that evolution sparks different metaphysical reflections, musings, and conclusions. Science teachers should not ignore such thinking, and we certainly should not pretend that such thinking is unimportant to students. Rather, this situation makes the teaching of origins a very good place for the implementation of methodological secularism.

By this, however, I do not mean some sort of "balanced treatment approach," as Creationists advocated for in the 1980s, or the "teach the controversy" approach of more recent years. But I do mean that classrooms need to allow for the inevitable metaphysical diversity among students. To accomplish this within the bounds of law, I have four rules for implementing methodological secularism in the science classroom. These are all articulated with respect to evolution, but the rules apply in principle to all science topics.

RULE 1: Teach Science, not Scientism.

Students and teachers need to understand the difference between science and scientism. A science popularizer like Michael Shermer, columnist for *Scientific America*, for example, is not someone to follow. He proudly announces that we are now in the age of science; that it is "scientism's shamans who command our veneration"; and that scientists today are our "premier mythmakers."[31] Indeed, since at least the 1700s there have been those who wished to assail religion, to lessen its prestige and influence, and to see science become the dominant factor in all persons' thinking. This is an attitude that has, not surprisingly, provoked conflict. However, as noted by Michael Ruse, such conflict is not a "simple clash between science and religion but rather between two religions,"[32] with Shermer, Dawkins, and others acting as the high priests or shamans for the new religion of scientism. The point is to recognize that science *does require* a metaphysic; and that moreover, there is not just one set of fundamental beliefs that will support science, but rather many. Science also has a limited scope in which it can work (there are questions it cannot answer) and it certainly does no harm to the enterprise of science that we carefully observe its limitations. Indeed, one of the great historical strengths of the natural sciences is that limitations *are* observed by scientists.

This rule should be the easiest for teachers to observe. For the most part, science teachers are not interested in extremism; they tend to realize that excessive claims on behalf of science only undercut one's arguments against the encroachment of Creationism and similar ideologies. The rule is nonetheless critical to the defense against any ideological co-opting of science.

RULE 2: Teach for Sound Understanding, not Belief.

Don't teach for belief. Don't preach. Understanding is critical; belief is not. This rule may be the hardest one for teachers to observe. After all, English teachers do not teach grammar that they think is not grammatical. History teachers do not teach history that they think is inaccurate. And science teachers do not teach science that they think incorrectly describes the workings of the natural world. Hence, teachers think—and indeed, expect—that their students will believe what they are taught. And this natural, *prima facie* opinion is held by others besides teachers, thus it can be no surprise that the very idea of not necessarily teaching for belief has been hotly debated in the professional journals.[33]

But common sense must prevail. People do not find all evidence equally compelling. The evidence that convinces a scientist may not convince non-scientists. People often have other evidences that are more compelling to them, or other authorities that are more trusted. Ignoring these realities is simply counterproductive because it leads students to feel that they are being indoctrinated rather than taught. Disbelief, moreover, does not bar understanding. Indeed, students are much more open to learning when they are confident that the teacher is not trying to "convert" them. Teachers must also recognize that student rejection of (say) evolution does not mean that those same students reject all of science. There are keen science students who nonetheless reject the validity of evolutionary theory[34] or one aspect or another of science. Moreover, it should be of some encouragement to teachers that although belief is up to the students, what one student believes today will likely change and develop over time. Ideas and beliefs evolve. So teachers ought to give students evidence to think about (Rule 3) and space to sort out the issues important to them (Rule 4), and belief will change and develop.

Though beyond the scope of this essay, Rule 2 can also be argued philosophically from the opposing perspectives of epistemological realism and instrumentalism. Most science teachers are natural realists (and I too have argued for realism in another venue[35]), but physicists, especially, hold instrumentalist epistemologies. Essentially, Rule 2 calls for an instrumentalist epistemology on an "as needed" basis.

RULE 3: Teach the Evidence.

This rule is simply good science teaching, but too often the science curriculum is what Joseph Schwab called a "rhetoric of conclusions."[36] The conclusions are needed (e.g., the outlines of the general theory of evolution); but without some introduction to the evidence that scientists adduce in support of theories such as evolution, student understanding of science will be weak. Worse, some students will conclude that the science of evolution is more an ideological stance than an evidence-based scientific theory, which is exactly the message of Young-earth Creationists. If we want skeptical students to develop confidence in the scientific soundness of theories such as evolution, Rule 2 requires Rule 3.

This rule should not be controversial. Scientific literacy according to such documents as the *National Science Education Standards* means that students learn both the facts and concepts of science along with the nature of science, meaning: how science works and what constitutes scientific knowledge. When a science teacher presents the fossil record, calculations on the age of the earth, and comparative anatomy of organisms (and so forth), it should be natural to ask what one can infer from these data. What is the best explanation for this vast array of data? The answer is evolution. Teaching science by moving from evidence and data to concepts and theory is the teaching of science by inquiry,[37] and it not only promotes better understanding but also minimizes slippage into ideology and indoctrination.

RULE 4: Give Students Time to Explore their own Ideas.

We do not need lessons on Intelligent Design and we do not need to examine facts that some think contradict evolution. But from metaphysical theory to epistemological theories of coherence to cognitive theories of conceptual change to democracy and the free exercise of ideas, it makes no sense to ignore ideas that students bring to the classroom, ideas that the students deem relevant, regardless of what their science teachers think. Science teachers need to acknowledge that this diversity of thought is very likely to exist, and to ask the students if they would like the opportunity to explore their own metaphysical questions of interest.[38] To do so creates a hospitable environment that will open possibilities for learning rather than closing them off. There are simple guidelines to follow. If a student wants to report on the "young age" of the earth, fine—but require that student to also study the standard evidences used by scientists to date the earth. In other words, insist that students consider all evidence, not a selected set. If a student wants to present a case for atheism based on science, this also is acceptable. But so is a case for theism. To put the guidelines another way, let students who wish to present science-based philosophical and metaphysical positions do so, and this includes traditionally religious positions. If they want to present some position regarding physical nature (e.g., there are no true transition fossils), they must show that they have read the *standard* scientific accounts.

Yes, Rule 4 may open the classroom door to Creationism and other highly sectarian ideas, but the approach is legal since students initiate whatever is brought to class and there is no hint of coercion or collusion. Openness has a price, however: sometimes ideas running counter to standard science will circulate. But the "closed" classroom does not stop this circulation; it only bars it from the classroom, which then has the side effect that some students will not seriously consider standard scientific evidences. The closed-door approach, the philosophical secularism approach, gives us the stalemate and conflict we have today.

Conclusion

Bringing methodological secularism to the science classroom makes the teaching of controversial subjects (such as evolution) considerably more complicated than teaching simple, uncontroversial subjects (for instance, the kinetic theory of gases, or respiration). One simply cannot take a rather unsophisticated internalist scientific perspective, as if nothing mattered but the science of the subject. On the other hand, adopting the stance of philosophical naturalism and philosophical secularism is both philosophically and pedagogically unsound. Science is turned into scientism; secular values are perverted. Moreover, philosophical secularism is unworkable in the vast majority of American public schools. Openness to student-initiated ideas, in contrast, defuses potential conflicts and leaves avenues open for student learning and growth—which otherwise would be shut off. Openness promotes democracy.

The Lincoln biographer Allen Guelzo wrote that Lincoln "struggled to be true to the two souls of American culture": one theistically religious and the other secular, commercial and enlightened. Guelzo wrote that these two souls of America "have often been locked in combat, only to withdraw after a brief battering reminds them that in America they have no choice but to co-exist." In recent decades, we, too, have been battering ourselves through litigation over what can and cannot be taught in school. It is past time to cease these hostilities and realize that there will not be any clear-cut victory for either side. The optimism of methodological secularism is that we learn to peacefully co-exist.

Endnotes

1. As well as followers of other religions, but I focus on Christianity since it is the dominant religion in the USA.

2. See W. M. McClay, "Two Concepts of Secularism," in *Religion Returns to the Public Square: Faith and Policy in America* (Washington, DC: Woodrow Wilson Center Press, 2003), 31-61.

3. It will be interesting to see the effects of Islam, which is spreading throughout Europe.

4. Two caveats: larger percentages of National Academy Fellows reject belief in God (Larson and Witham, 1998) and the nature of public beliefs about God show change.

5. For a more complete examination of polling data, see Barry Kosmin and Ariela Keysar's *Religion in a Free Market* (Ithaca, NY: Paramount Market Publishers, Inc., 2006).

6. Consistently 95% or more.

7. Princeton Religious Research Center (1996), 20.

8. C. P. Toumey, "Evolution and secular humanism," *Journal of the American Academy of Religion*, 61 (2) (1993), 275-301.

9. The Becket Fund for Religious Liberty, 2003.

10. Pollingreport.com (2007); Pollingreport.com (2004); Religioustolerance.org (2005).

11. CBS poll, 2005.

12. FOX News poll, 2004.

13. For a brief but excellent account of this revolutionary period, see Toumey (1993).

14. Guide to the Darwin Centennial Celebration Records 1959 (2006).

15. For example, *McLean v. Arkansas Board of Education* (1982).

16. *Kitzmiller v. Dover Area School District* (2005).

17. No one should be fooled by these self proclaimed warriors for reason. The cognitive processes of reasoning, as powerful and essential as they are, have no natural immunity to intolerance and willful ignorance to which all humanity are susceptible, as so clearly exemplified by these three authors.

18. D. C. Dennett, "The Bright Stuff," *The New York Times* online, http://www.nytimes.com/2003/07/12/opinion/12DENN.html?th, March 14, 2007.

19. C. S. Lewis, *The Abolition of Man* (New York, NY: MacMillan Publishing Co., 1947), 91.

20. W. W. Cobern, "Worldview Theory and Science Education Research," *NARST Monograph No. 3* (Manhattan, KS: National Association for Research in Science Teaching, 1991); Cobern, "The Nature of Science and the Role of Knowledge and Belief," *Science & Education* 9 (3) (2000), 219-246.

21. Tillich, 1964.

22. By no means is this an exclusively Christian perspective, but one shared by many.

23. A. Salam, *Ideals and Realities: Selected Essays of Abdus Salam* (Singapore: World Scientific, 1984); F. S. Collins, *The Language of God: A Scientist Presents Evidence for Belief* (New York: Simon & Schuster, 2006).

24. Galileo Galilei, Letter to the Grand Duchess Christina of Tuscany, 1615.

25. McClay, "Two Concepts of Secularism," in *Religion Returns to the Public Square: Faith and Policy in America*, McClay, H. Heclo and W. M. McClay, eds., 31-61.

26. See Cobern, "ID Hysteria says More about some People's Freudian 'ID' than about Science," *Canadian Journal of Science, Mathematics, and Technology Education*, 7 (2/3), 276-262; see also Cobern, "One Christian's Perspective on Creation and Evolution," SLCSP Working Paper #176 (Kalamazoo, MI: Western Michigan University), http://www.wmich.edu/slcsp/SLCSP176/SLCSP176.pdf.

27. Quoted in E. J. Larson, "God and the Galapagos?" http://www.metanexus.net/archives/message_fs.asp?ARCHIVEID=4069, August 27, 2001.

28. Weinberg, 1988.

29. Larson, "God and the Galapagos?"

30. Ibid.

31. M. Shermer, "The Shamans of Scientism," *Scientific American*, 286 (6) (2002).

32. M. Ruse, *The Evolution-Creation Struggle* (Cambridge, MA: Harvard University Press, 2005), 80.

33. Cobern, "Point: Belief, Understanding, and the Teaching of Evolution," *Journal of Research in Science Teaching*, 31 (5) (1994): 583-590; M. U. Smith, "Counterpoint: Belief, Understanding, and the Teaching of Evolution." *Journal of Research in Science Teaching*, 31 (5) (1994): 591-597; for a though treatment of the issues, see Cobern, 2000.

34. Cobern and Loving, "Thinking about Science and Christian Orthodox Beliefs: a Survey Study of Preservice elementary teachers," in *Proceedings of the 2005 International Conference on the History and Philosophy of Science Teaching* (Leeds: International History, Philosophy, Sociology & Science Teaching Conference, 2005), M. Nott, ed.

35. See Cobern and Loving, "An Essay for Educators: Epistemological Realism Really is Common Sense," *Science & Education* (2007).

36. J. J. Schwab, "The Teaching of Science as Enquiry," *The Inglis Lecture* (Cambridge, MA: Harvard University Press, 1962).

37. National Research Council, *Inquiry and the National Science Education Standards: A Guide for Teaching and Learning* (Washington, DC: National Academy Press, 2000).

38. I refer, of course, only to secondary school and higher education. These issues are not so relevant at the elementary school science education level but where they are a very different approach would be needed.

6. Implementing Methodological Secularism: The Teaching and Practice of Science in Contentious Times

David E. Henderson

The central problem for public secularism has been identified by Cobern[1] as a philosophically naked public square. In this chapter, I shall pursue this theme further in three areas. These are, firstly, the problem of philosophical secularism; secondly, how the science courses I have been developing with the support of the Institute for the Study of Secularism in Society and Culture (ISSSC) meet Cobern's four rules for implementing methodological secularism in the classroom; and, finally, how we can advance this debate.

Here, I shall consider the specific question of whether the current intellectual battle over science—a battle that pits science against religion in the U.S.—is really necessary.

Philosophical Secularism: Science or Religion?

Cobern's formulation of two forms of secularism is quite compelling. His distinction makes sense, and it provides a mechanism to identify when secularism is on a sound scientific and philosophical footing, and when it is not. It creates a useful parallel between two kinds of secularism and the two kinds of naturalism, philosophical and methodological, practiced by scientists. Clearly, all science must operate at the level of methodological naturalism. We cannot invoke God for things we don't yet understand. And a religion that depends on placing God in the gaps will struggle as the gaps are closed by new scientific discoveries. However, philosophical naturalism, like philosophical secularism, is not a position that can be tested by scientific experiment. It is, rather, a matter of faith.

Richard Dawkins has been a leading proponent of philosophical secularism in the scientific community. He has popularized the powerful biology of random mutation and natural selection as a kind of scientism. It should not be called Darwinism, however, since Darwin would certainly not recognize it as his. A more accurate term would be "Dawkinism." As a scientist, I find Dawkins' arguments unconvincing. Science cannot prove a negative. When scientists make categorical negative statements, e.g., "there is no God," "Chlorofluorocarbons (CFCs) are completely safe for the environment," and "Bisphenol A has no negative effects on humans"—one needs to be alert. Absolute positive, exclusionary statements, such as "random mutation is the only mechanism of speciation of life," also contain the same untestable character. And trying to extend the beautiful theory of Darwin beyond biology does a disservice to the science.

I made the above statements about two chemicals to show the danger of categorical negative statements. In the 1970s, CFCs were seen as perfectly safe and were viewed as some of the most ideal chemicals for their applications. They were non-toxic, long-lasting, and inert. By the 1980s, evidence was growing that they were disastrous to the stratospheric ozone layer. The 1989 Montreal Protocol has led to their gradual elimination. Scientists estimate that it will take 50-100 years to undo the damage we have done with these chemicals. There is growing evidence that Bisphenol A, which is found in the blood of 96% of the American population, has clear negative effects on the hormonal system of people. Recent findings suggest that there are at least three major negative effects: early sexual maturation, obesity, and Type II diabetes.[2] One need only look at the statistics on these problems to suspect a causal link exists even though it has yet to be scientifically proven. We all ingest Bisphenol A when we eat and drink things that have been stored in common plastics and metal containers that are lined with plastics. It is detectable in virtually all canned foods and beverages. The US-EPA's decision, in the late 1990s, to begin regulating hormone mimics is a classic example of how questions no one ever thought to ask can lead to new science. The FDA has not yet followed suit for food packaging and Bisphenol A, but pressure is mounting for it to take action.

In the case of evidence for God, it is not clear that science has the tools to even ask the question of whether a supernatural, spiritual entity exists. If science is the study of the "natural," then it almost by definition excludes the supernatural. How could a scientist develop the confidence to assert that there is no God? I believe it is only scientifically tenable to say that, given the tools at our disposal and the experiments we have been able to conceive, we have not found any positive evidence for God. A scientist who makes a categorical negative statement, about God or anything else, is not speaking as a scientist but making a statement of faith, belief without evidence. This is especially true if our universe is part of a space-time with at least 11 dimensions, of which we directly perceive only four, as proposed by String Theory. Philosophical naturalism is always suspect due to its insistence on negative (and hence unprovable) statements. Similarly, philosophical secularism is a faith system rather than something supported by scientific evidence.

Francis Collins, Director of the Human Genome Project, argues in his recent book *The Language of God*[3] that there is evidence for the supernatural based on the existence of the Moral Law among human cultures and the human quest for the sacred. While one can argue with his logic, the fact that Collins even makes this argument demonstrates that scientists are not in complete agreement about the absence of evidence for God. This may explain why a significant number of scientists are also believers.

Science Curriculum

The second question I wish to address is: How can a science curriculum meet the needs of the average student in college or high school? What should students who are not going to be professional scientists know about science? This raises a deeper question of what science is. I would argue that the core of science is the *process* we use to determine which observations and theories are closest to the truth, and which should be discarded. By "process," I don't mean the stylized "scientific method" that appears in the opening chapter of most science texts. Rather, I mean the messy process of argument and conflict between competing ideas and between competing evidence: the nuts and bolts of science. Science is a human activity, and the progress of science is accompanied by all the foibles of humanity: pride, greed, envy, etc. In spite of these human weaknesses, better theories will eventually prevail against those that do not hold up to examination. Some theories, like plate tectonics, took decades to be accepted by the scientific community. Other theories, like relativity, were quickly accepted, but will require centuries to actually test in full detail. Still other theories, like evolution, have had their ups and downs, as evidence accumulated and the theory was refined in light of new knowledge. In fact, the evolution of life is an example of a theory that is still developing rich new levels of evidence and is filled with uncertainty.

Cobern's first rule is to teach science, not scientism. This implies a focus on conflict and process more than on the specific current theories. Theories may change, but the process continues. If students are to "believe" in anything, it should be that this messy process will ultimately produce correct insights and eliminate incorrect ones. But it is not necessary that students "believe" that the current theories are the final word. If scientists themselves believed this, there would not be much left to work on. One of my chemistry professors once told our class that when scientists start to "believe" their theories, they stop being scientists. The implication is that we use theories, but they should never become articles of faith, only tools for explaining our observations.

Cobern's second rule—to teach understanding rather than belief—implies that students need to see the reasoning behind the current generation of theories. This may be the hardest thing to do in a science class. Much of the evidence is far too complicated for students to interpret. The evidence used by scientists has moved far beyond the things we can actually see. We now have digits on readouts and computer data from sensors far removed from our direct ability to perceive them. There is a sense in which scientists now place great faith in their instruments and probes—things that were not needed in past centuries. This situation makes it harder to apply Cobern's third rule—to actually teach the evidence—than one would think. This makes the teaching of the process all the more important. Students do not need to trust the actual data, such as tracks in a bubble chamber at CERN or the complex set of four color tracings from a DNA sequencer. Rather, they need to trust that scientists, as a group, are contentious enough to argue over these things until they have them correct. It is better for them to see science as a big argument over evidence than as of some sort of monolithic dogma, a collection of facts.

Courses for non-science majors tend to fall into the trap of teaching belief rather than understanding. It is much harder to bring evidence to these classes. Often, courses for non-majors are taught without labs. It is difficult to develop a sense of evidence—or understand the limits of evidence—without the experience of collecting and evaluating evidence. And, of course, the mere existence of labs does not guarantee this either. Many labs are simply exercises in proving the obvious. This failure to really address the process of science does a disservice to science, and may be partly responsible for both the dismal public view of science that we see in the political arena and the lack of interest by students.

A final problem with science teaching is that most science courses avoid the moral implications of the science they teach, and discourage students from asking questions about science and morality. As a result, science majors rarely encounter the larger issues of morality, ethics, or global responsibility—issues germane to science—anywhere in their major courses. I believe that scientists' reluctance to discuss these issues in the classroom is part of our problem. We argue that there is just too much that students need to know to find time for these "secondary" topics. But in doing so, we make our courses, and the study of science, less interesting and less relevant for our students—and then we bemoan the lack of interest in science by the very students we have failed to serve. Redressing this trend requires that we follow Cobern's fourth rule: "Give students time to explore their own ideas."

A former student recently told me that the class he spent on climate change during an introductory chemistry course was the only time he was excited about studying chemistry. Covering the big issues does matter.

Reacting to the Past™[4] Science Courses: One solution

I have been developing two courses as part of a larger effort to use a new pedagogy called *Reacting to the Past*, with the goal of making college science courses more engaging.

I think that these courses succeed in following Cobern's four rules. They put the large questions on the table first, and ask students to use evidence to find answers. They do not avoid controversy or try to teach the controversy. Instead, they use controversy to teach the evidence. They also demonstrate that argument between conflicting ideas is at the core of science, and they allow students to participate in this conflict using historical events.

The "Reacting" pedagogy was developed by Professor Mark Carnes at Barnard University; it has now spread to over 100 colleges and universities. The original purpose of the "Reacting" approach was to teach general education courses in the humanities. But I quickly realized that the same approach could be used to teach science as well. This led me to begin developing what we now call "Reacting Science" courses. We now have four such courses in active use, with several more in various stages of planning.

The heart of the "Reacting" approach is to involve students in elaborate simulations of important historical events. The simulations are referred to as "games" and the students play roles in these games. The simulations are not scripted. Students are given defined roles; they must internalize the goals of the person they represent and determine how best to reach their objectives in the game, based on what was known at the time of the event. When students play "Reacting" games, no two classes ever follow the same trajectory or reach the same outcome. At the core of this approach is the idea that history is contingent upon people and events. Most games include a certain amount of randomness to simulate the degree to which unpredictable events affect historical outcomes. History is replete with examples of seemingly trivial events that changed everything. The fact that the wheel broke on the carriage King Louis XVI used to escape from Paris led to his capture. Had the wheel not broken, he might have reached the army coming to rescue him and the French Revolution might have failed. Similarly, in the *Evolution in Kansas* game, the election of a new Board of Education is contingent not only upon how convincing the candidates are, but also on the weather, which will determine how many people go to the polls to vote.

One powerful feature of the "Reacting" pedagogy relates to Cobern's fourth rule: "Give students time to explore their own ideas." A problem with modern college students is their reluctance to actually put their ideas on the table in public discussion. Students are increasingly reluctant to take a position in class that may put them at odds with their professor or classmates. This makes it hard to implement rule four in classes. The "Reacting" pedagogy solves this problem by assigning the various positions to different students. These students then present these positions using the voice of their character. The result is that they are personally insulated from *owning* the positions, while at the same time, they are free to discuss them and have them challenged by those representing other positions. This produces a free-flowing discussion in which students feel no pressure to state personal beliefs. At the end of the process, students can ultimately endorse a position as their own based on their active participation in the arguments.

There are four "Reacting Science" games currently available[5]:

- *Evolution in Kansas—1999*, by David E. Henderson (and Rob Pennock in the next revision).

- *Acid Rain in Europe—1979-1989*, by David E. Henderson and Susan K. Henderson.

- *Trial of Galileo, The: Aristotelianism, the "New Cosmology" and the Catholic Church*, 1616-1633, by Fred Purnell, Mark Carnes, and Michael Petterson. Prentice Hall: 2008.

- *Charles Darwin, the Copley Medal, and the Rise of Naturalism*, by Marsha Driscoll, Elizabeth Dunn, Dann Siems, and Kamran Swanson.

All of these games involve conflicting interpretations and theories. All provide the opportunity for students to engage in Cobern's third rule: Consider the evidence. And all involve issues of the authority of evidence and the conflicts of philosophy, religion, and economics, issues that often color the interpretation of evidence in the scientific community. The *Darwin* game explicitly considers the nature of science and naturalism within the roles and debates of the game. Both *Galileo* and *Kansas* examine the conflict that sometimes arises when religion adopts a specific position on a scientific issue and attempts to maintain that position in the face of mounting evidence to the contrary. *Acid Rain* examines the utilitarian philosophical position of most societies and how it comes into conflict with the need to protect the environment, the "Commons" on which our lives depend. It also shows the power that economic interests have to hold on to felicitous theories—much the way that religious interests do. The structure of all the games insures that all positions are examined and that students have the opportunity to think about them and make personal decisions. Whether the students reach the position preferred by the faculty is not a part of the process, though the discussion after the game allows the current consensus position to be presented. Thus, there is no pressure for belief, only for understanding. I will now discuss, in more detail, how the conflicts in each game play themselves out.

In *Evolution in Kansas*, students pretend to be members of the Kansas Board of Education, and must address, using science available in 2000-2001, whether macro-evolution and Big Bang cosmology should be taught in the Kansas schools. Students are assigned various philosophical and religious positions that were represented in Kansas at the time. Some are New Earth Creationists who interpret the Christian scriptures literally; some believe that there is a way to reconcile all our observations about the world with the biblical descriptions of the Book of Genesis. Other, less conservative roles accept the general findings of science, but believe in a synthesis of science and religion, as Francis Collins suggests. Still others approach the issue from the viewpoint of non-theistic scientists like Dawkins, and from other religious perspectives, specifically Hinduism.

All students in the course read portions of Darwin's *The Origin of Species* and Margulis' *Microcosmos*[6] to get a sense of the science involved. Both of these texts provide evidence to support their theories. Margulis' theory of symbiotic evolution was as controversial when first proposed as Darwin's. Both theories are now accepted as forming part of the fabric of evolution. It is hoped that students come away with the understanding that there is still much to be learned, but that each part contributes to the whole. Students also discuss the basic ideas of cosmology and learn a little bit about quantum mechanics. They then research evidence to support their various positions. Finally, over the course of three weeks, the students debate the evidence. They present the best case they can and do their best to find weaknesses in their opponents' arguments. A small group of undecided students holds the balance of power on the Board of Education and must decide which group presents the stronger case. The simulation is made more realistic by the inclusion of other issues that normally arise in education discussions, money for special programs, how to teach reading, etc. Final decisions by the undecided students are based not only on the quality of the arguments, but also on political considerations. After the simulation game is completed, one or two classes are used to bring the class up to date on the current understanding of evolution and the current cosmological theories. Several short lab experiments are also available to help students understand how scientists determine the age of objects. The Margulis text is included in part because it challenges the simple random mutation ideas of Darwin and opens students up to a complex interplay of forces at the center of evolution. It also shows the controversy within science over exactly how new species arise.

My second reacting game, *Acid Rain in Europe*, is set in the 1980s, in the context of the discussions over acid rain and the steps needed to protect the environment from airborne pollutants. The *Acid Rain in Europe* game introduces students to ecology and asks fundamental questions about the place of humanity with respect to the environment. The students begin by learning about acid-base chemistry and how acids are formed due to air pollution. This includes optional short lab experiments, which include actual measurements on local rain water. They also examine various philosophical positions related to the environment. Readings include Lovelock's book, *Gaia,* and material from Plato, Aristotle, Descartes, and modern authors including Aldo Leopold (*Sand County Almanac*[7]). The Lovelock book is particularly instructive and has been quite controversial. Lovelock begins with his evaluation of the evidence for life on Mars. His description of how he used the evidence to conclude life was not present is a nice example of how one should interpret evidence. Lovelock then extends the conversation to the nature of life on earth. The very fact that the book, as with the Margulis text in the Kansas game, was so controversial introduces students to the diversity of opinions that are the essence of the scientific process.

In the first stage of the Acid Rain game, the controversy focuses on various philosophical positions on the environment. Some students are assigned teleological and utilitarian positions, and some are assigned positions based in *Deep Ecology*.[8] They debate whether nations are responsible for the effects of their air pollution on other nations. Students then argue over the science of whether pollution from coal-fired power plants is causing damage to forests and lakes thousands of miles away. Using the evidence available at the start of the game in 1979, it is relatively easy to argue that the evidence is too weak to support expensive action. The British faction in the game, like the British government of the time, makes this argument very forcefully. During the 10-year span covered by the game, the evidence accumulates until it is undeniable that trans-boundary emissions are causing environmental damage. Thus, the gradual accumulation of evidence and the way that this changes policy is made clear. This accumulation of evidence is presented through new data provided to the various factions, along with instructions from their governments to change their positions. The British faction continues to hold out against environmental protection to the bitter end, in spite of the evidence, for political and economic reasons. In politics as in science, there are always holdouts.

As in the Kansas game, students find evidence and bring it to the classroom. The short laboratory experiments allow students to learn how data are acquired through experiment and also to see the uncertainty and messiness of real experimental data. They are also forced to deal quantitatively with large bodies of data on pollution levels and economics and to understand the technology of power production and pollution control.

Galileo and the New Cosmology includes experiments on astronomy, optics, and geometry. Students participate in the clash between the cosmology of Ptolemy and that of Galileo, Kepler, and Copernicus. Again, evidence—in the form of Galileo's excellent observations and interpretation—is a major focus of the arguments. The conflict between Ptolemy and Copernicus is an excellent example of two different, and seemingly equally successful, interpretations of the same evidence. Students learn about the parallax of stars—which could conclusively settle the question of which cosmology is correct. If the earth moves, the stars should appear to shift position slightly during the course of the year. Galileo was not able to find evidence for parallax. This is an important example of evidence that is missing, and the need to reach a conclusion without definitive evidence. It was not until centuries later that telescopes became powerful enough to measure the small effects that exist.

In *Charles Darwin, the Copley Medal, and the Rise of Naturalism*, students examine the evidence on evolution—both for and against—that was available in Darwin's own time. The simulation is set in the British Royal Society, as it debates whether Darwin should receive the Copley Medal. Much of the debate focuses on the nature of science. One issue in the game is a proposal to do scientific experiments to test the efficacy of prayer. This issue arose due to the illness of Prince Albert. This discussion allows for consideration of how one would do controls for such an experiment and how one would interpret the results. Recent efforts to do just this experiment have led to very unusual results. In one study, the heart attack patients who were prayed for—and knew they were prayed for—had significantly worse outcomes than those who were not. But the very nature of the experiment makes it almost impossible to interpret the data. I think that these courses offer a fresh way to introduce science as the study of evidence— without flinching from the fundamental issues that scientific discoveries raise. The "Reacting to the Past" pedagogy has been demonstrated to increase student involvement with the material and turn the power of peer pressure into a positive force for student engagement. Rather than teaching the controversy, the goal is to use the controversy to teach the evidence. And the controversy is used to add intensity to the science and provoke students' interest.

Where do We Go from Here?

Much of the public warfare between secularism and theism is the product of extremists on both sides, and the situation can certainly be improved if scientists return to Methodological Secularism. Ronald Numbers, in his book *The Creationists*, argues that the push to enshrine Creation science is largely a reaction to philosophical secularists like Dawkins. While it is certainly within the rights of Dawkins and others to say whatever they wish in the public forum, the scientific community has every right to expect a level of restraint in using scientific credentials to promote non-scientific claims. Dawkins' statements about the absence of God are metaphysical, not scientific. The use of scientific credentials to make metaphysical statements should be discouraged within the scientific community.

Within religion, there is a close parallel that reflects the divide between methodological and philosophical secularism that Cobern has identified. The extreme fundamentalist forms of all faiths make the same error seen in philosophical secularism. While they cast their faith in terms of positive evidence and belief, such claims are based on inherently negative statements, such as "there is no God but mine" or "there is no way to worship God but mine." These are statements of faith; they cannot be tested and they place limits on the power of the God they worship. They lead to religious intolerance and absolutism. By contrast, many people of faith approach their theism similarly to the methodological secularist. They live as Theists but they refrain from making un-testable negative statements about what their God can or cannot do or allow. The humility of this position is analogous to the humility of scientists who constantly face the uncertainty in their theories.

The moderate factions in both science and religion would seem to hold the key to peace and reconciliation. It is vital that scientists speak out against metaphysical statements by scientists, and equally vital that people of faith reject the exclusive statements of fundamentalists in favor of more inclusiveness. The battle between moderates and extremists plays out in every sphere: religion, politics, metaphysics, and environmentalism. This is not a battle that will be won or lost, but one that must continue to be fought throughout the generations.

Conclusion

Conflict is an integral part of the process of science. While most scientists will probably never be engaged in the most vicious arguments that occur during a major paradigm shift, all scientists participate in the process of collecting evidence to test our understanding of the world. To teach science as anything other than an ongoing process is to do a disservice to the next generation of scientists. In fact, this practice is at the root of much of our society's misunderstanding of science. Cobern's four rules for science teaching are basic to insuring that science education, both for scientists and non-scientists, is done in a way that moves us forward. The "Reacting to the Past" approach to teaching science is one example of how this can be done. Both science majors and non-majors will benefit from the focus on how conflicts are resolved and how other factors in our culture impact the practice of science.

ENDNOTES

1. See Cobern, Chapter 5.

2. Elizabeth Grossman, "Chemicals May Play Role in Rise in Obesity," *Washington Post*, March 12, 2007.

3. Francis S. Collins, *The Language of God: A Scientist Presents Evidence for Belief* (New York: Free Press, 2006).

4. "Reacting to the Past" is a trademark of Barnard College.

5. Game materials not yet published by Prentice Hall may be obtained for use free of charge at www.barnard.edu/reacting.

6. Lynn Margulis and Doren Sagan, *Microcosmos: Four Billion Years of Microbial Evolution* (Berkeley: University of California Press, 1986).

7. Aldo Leopold, *A Sand County Almanac* (Ballantine Books, 1986).

8. Bill Devall and George Sessions, *Deep Ecology: Living as if Nature Mattered* (Salt Lake City: Gibbs Smith, 1985).

7. U.S. Public Education: A Battleground from the Ivory Tower to First Grade

Benjamin Beit-Hallahmi

S igmund Freud identified two major blows to "human megalomania"—blows that destroyed our long-held self-image as unique and superior.[1] The first blow was the Copernican revolution, which deprived humans of their place at the center of the universe, telling them that earth was in a remote corner of one galaxy among billions. Then came Charles Darwin, putting us in our place as part of the animal kingdom, with no special creation needed for our appearance on earth.

These blows to our natural narcissism, which grew out of the methodical use of what we now call naturalism, were unlikely to pass without resistance. Accepting them demands that we think in ways that are quite literally unnatural, and that involve taking a radically novel vantage point when looking at the world and ourselves. What is remarkable is that quite a few humans have embraced, or at least accepted, the unnatural behaviors that lie at the basis of what we call, in everyday usage, science. But the impact of human resistance to these narcissistic blows is still reverberating around us.

In this chapter I will try to place the debate over science education in the United States in the context of a wider, continuing struggle over Enlightenment values and secularization. This struggle has historically involved all levels of education, which are interlinked, starting at the top. What happens at research universities, while seemingly of concern to a small elite, has an impact on public education through a formal process of credentialing and through the enormous authority of science in modern society.

The Phylogenesis of Religion

Anthropomorphism is our most natural cognitive strategy. Seeing the world as we experience ourselves subjectively is a natural step of generalizing from what we already know to what we need to explore, but the limitations of this strategy are obvious. Animism, one form of anthropomorphism, is a process in which humans understand the world around them by assuming that all creatures and objects share with them the subjective experience of consciousness, as well as intentionality. This can be observed in young children, who, after accidentally hitting a table, will hit back at it, meaning to inflict pain. Later on, there is an explicit belief that all objects are endowed with a "soul," sharing with humans the experience of consciousness and volition. Animism as a cognitive strategy is the starting point of all belief systems, including religion and science.

Religion, a belief system premised on the notion of an invisible world of spirits, has been around for possibly 100,000 years, and has changed relatively little. The irreducible core common to all religions contains the belief in spirits inhabiting an invisible world, and claims about our relationship with them. "It is the premise of every religion—and this premise is religion's defining characteristic— that souls, supernatural beings, and supernatural forces exist."[2] Religion as an institution is the mediator between the supernatural world and the visible human and natural world.[3]

In promoting the idea of an eternal soul, every religion promises us a victory over the most disturbing element of our biological nature: the finality of death. Most religions also offer us eschatological visions about a Messiah who will solve the problems of death and injustice once and for all.

The Coming of Naturalism

Naturalism can be defined simply as looking at the world non-animistically, a method that humanity has developed in its search for an effective control of nature. Naturalistic reasoning is counterintuitive, unnatural, and hard to develop, as it requires overcoming innate cognitive strategies.[4] Because it is innate and intuitive, animism does not have to be taught. What we have to teach are non-animistic ways of looking at the world. What we call science, or academic research, is made up of the institutionalization of unnatural and counterintuitive modes of thinking.

In everyday life, most of us use a combination of animistic and non-animistic thinking, depending on our momentary level of egocentrism and anxiety, and on the task at hand. Most humans still hang on to animism and notions of design and intentionality as their intuitive way of explaining events around them, but they (passively) accept the independence from animism of academic research and its derivative technologies.

A naturalism-animism conflict is today most often expressed in the context of discussions about the relationship between religion and science. All religions share the common denominator of institutionalized animism, while all academic research fields share the common denominator that they attempt to look at events around us non-animistically.

"Religion" and "science" are, of course, loose and rough abstractions. In reality, there are perhaps 10,000 living religions in this world, and there are thousands of academic disciplines and sub-disciplines. All secular education, and not just science education, is about teaching counterintuitive ways of looking at the human and non-human worlds. In every public school subject, and not just science classes, explanations are based on naturalism. But when we think of science education in modern school systems, what we have in mind are the rudiments of natural science paradigms.

Secularization and the Phylogenesis of Science

Academic research is an amazingly recent historical development and its evolution is tied to the historical process of secularization, which is both pervasive and relative, and through which both society and individuals have moved away from the dominance of religious institutions and ideation. In all industrial societies today, religion, which was once uniform, collectivistic, public, ascribed, and inherited, is today pluralist, individualistic, privatized, and sometimes chosen. Privatization is the most important change, overriding all other dimensions. The possibility of choice and preference in religious matters is a modern phenomenon, another symptom of the decline of religious power.

This decline of religion as a social institution has been connected with the rise of science, which came into being with the weakening of religious authority. For the past 500 years, religious doctrines have been dealt severe blows by the developing sciences. The process of the decline of religion and the rise of science has been eloquently described by Frazer: "For ages the army of spirits, once so near, has been receding farther and farther from us, banished by the magic wand of science from hearth and home."[5]

The secularization of education, at all levels, is one of the most important aspects of secularization in general. Universal education for the masses is a modern, secular ideal. Historically, higher education (like all education) was dominated by religious content. Universities in both medieval Europe and the Islamic world started in the Middle Ages as religious institutions. Higher education in the United States used to be primarily religious, producing mostly clergy. Such leading institutions as Harvard, Yale, Princeton, and Columbia were founded as religious colleges.

All academic fields, from anthropology to zoology, practice methodological atheism: any supernaturalist explanations are excluded from discussion.

Academics do not assume purpose or design, whether in nature, or in history, beyond human designs. A researcher may privately believe in divine purpose explanations, but trying to include them in any academic publication will lead to ridicule.

Graffin and Provine[6] reported the responses of 149 prominent evolutionary scientists, members of 28 national academies worldwide, to a questionnaire on evolution and religion. One hundred and seven of them supported the view that religion has developed with the biological evolution of *Homo sapiens*. These researchers could see no conflict between religion and evolution, simply because they regarded the former as another product of the latter, and so it could be studied and understood with the help of standard evolutionary theories.

The Academic Ethos

Merton[7] described the norms of academic culture as made up of universalism (claims to truth are evaluated in terms of impersonal criteria, and not on the basis of personal charateristics), communism (the common ownership of scientific discoveries, rewarded by recognition and esteem), disinterestedness (acting in ways that outwardly appear to be selfless) and organized skepticism (ideas must be tested and are subject to rigorous and structured community scrutiny). This unique and common culture of academia is shared by all fields of research, regardless of specific research questions and methods. Both history and chemistry have the same ethos. What Merton has described is an antiauthoritarian *weltanschauung*, which is clearly tied to Enlightenment ideals (or even an Enlightenment political program). Hollinger[8] showed that Merton's portrayal of the academic ethos was developed in the context of the fight for democracy in the 1930s and 1940s.

Research on the personalities of eminent scientists has shown that they were all recognized as unusually gifted as children. In addition, they were characterized as rebels, antiauthoritarian and counterdependent, who showed no respect for convention and tradition. It should be noted that most of this research has been done on individuals who were among the most eminent in both natural and human sciences.[9]

Further examination shows that the academy is a bastion of the Enlightenment vision, and that includes secularity. The religionist and eminent historian Huston Smith observed in 2005 that "The university today is uncompromisingly secular" and that in American society, "religion is everywhere, except in the intelligentsia, the people who rule our country, and in the media."[10] The academic world is indeed committed to Enlightenment values, and the values and commitments of the academic elite will have a decisive impact on education at all levels.

The Struggle to Secularize Public Education

Writing about the Scopes trial of 1925, Hofstadter[11] offered us a historical framing for the current struggles over science education in the United States:

> That the issue centered over the place of evolution in the public high school was itself evidence of the degree to which modernism had been brought down from the level of elite consciousness and made a part of popular consciousness. The battle over evolution in education had been fought out once before, in the colleges and universities, where conservative clergymen had tried during the three decades after 1860 to stem the tide of Darwinism. But there it had taken place at the elite level, and the inevitable losses sustained by the anti-evolutionists did not touch the vitals of the fundamentalists. Few of the true believers, after all, have attended college, and those who did could still seek out the backwater schools that had been kept pure from the infection of *The Origin of Species.* By the 1920's, however, the teaching of evolution, moving down the educational ladder, had overtaken high schools.

The battle over secularization in the academic world has been fought and won.[12] The victory over animism has been decisive and has led to the complete secularization of elite institutions, a process then imitated by lesser ones. The skirmishes over school prayer and the teaching of evolution over the past 50 years are all part of the continuing Secularization War in the United States. This Secularization War was fought not only over education. The greatest conservative defeats in the *Kulturkampf,* according to Hofstadter,[13] were the end of Prohibition in 1933 and the end of segregation following the 1954 *Brown* decision. The last great victory of radical conservatives was the defeat of the Equal Rights Amendment in the 1970s.

What we can observe is a continuing struggle for the secularization of public schools. The struggle has been long and costly, but its direction is unmistakable. Almost every encounter between the secular elite and the forces of tradition ends up with a victory for the former, with a series of uninterrupted defeats in the courts starting in 1925 in Kansas.

The forgotten struggle over religious activities in the public schools should be recalled to appreciate this process. A major historical struggle for secularizing all public schools systems in the United States ended with resounding triumph on June 17, 1963. In *Engel v. Vitale,*[14] the Supreme Court ruled that the New York Board of Regents could not require the daily recitation of prayers in the schools. In *Abington School District v. Schempp,*[15] the Supreme Court ruled that any Bible reading in the public schools was unconstitutional. The impact of the

Schempp decision can only be compared with that of the 1954 *Brown* decision, and both are related to the same social and historical forces. What is forgotten is that before the 1963 *Schempp* decision, Bible readings and organized prayers were common in public schools, and not only in the "Bible belt." *Engel* and *Schempp* had to do with a New York City suburb and with a Philadelphia suburb.

A small number of secular activists have won the Secularization War by using the Federal Courts successfully. The more numerous Christian activists have not been able to use their political clout against the *de facto* Enlightenment coalition of science and secularism. Opinion polls show that more than 60% of U.S. adults oppose the ban on school prayer and support some form of official religious activity in the schools. Resistance to the secularization of public education took the form of non-compliance and evasion, which meant that in many schools, especially in the South, Bible readings and prayers led by teachers were still a reality after 1963. Over the past five decades, such activities have become rare, as secularization kept marching on.[16]

The recent challenges to the teaching of evolution seem to follow the great historical loss by the religious right over religious activities in the schools. Legal moves by supporters of secularism have resulted in further defeats for the anti-modernity forces. *McLean v. Arkansas Board of Education*[17] was a milestone that defined the *Kulturkampf* in so many words as being waged between fundamentalism and science. In the 1987 *Edwards v. Aguillard* case, the U.S. Supreme Court ruled against a "creation science," and *Kitzmiller et al. v. Dover Area School District*[18] became the last stand of the Creationists.

Ann Coulter, a best-selling author and a prominent spokeswoman for the Christian right, has stated that "government schools" are the liberal equivalent of churches, and that public school teachers are the liberal clergy.[19] This is quite striking, and shows that public education is still an issue, because it is secular and has become more so. The conservative challenge is really about the secularity of public education, and not just about the teaching of evolution. The Coulter thesis proves that for the religious right, the issue is indeed basic Enlightenment values and the nature of public education.

At the most general level we may speak about two parties in the culture war: One is the party of intuition, animism, anthropocentricism, and authority, and the other is the party of the de-animization of nature, modernity, individualism, and universalism. The U.S. cultural landscape offers two major strategies for the "religion-science conflict." The first, and more visible, response is confrontation. This stems out of fundamentalism, which challenges naturalism and the Enlightenment openly and directly. Among liberal and better educated Protestants, the chosen strategy is accommodation, sometimes leading to a curious fantasy of fusion and reconciliation.

Why Evolution?

Biology is part of the challenge to religious cosmology when it offers a theory of the development of species, including mankind. Geology and astrophysics present another challenge when they account for the creation of the universe.[20] In 1999, the Kansas State Board of Education decided to eliminate mention of the Big Bang theory, as well as evolution, from its curriculum.[21]

Evolution, as Ronald Reagan correctly observed, is just a theory, like everything else in science. Most of us cannot follow its intricacies and implications, but at the most accessible level, it is clear that it denies any credence to creation myths and anthropocentric belief systems. The specific assumptions of the evolution paradigm are a threat to all religions, beyond the account of human descent from other species. It assumes no design, no intentionality, and no guiding hand, but rather randomness and purposelessness, with events only subject to the impersonal, natural laws of physics and chemistry. The debate is indeed about an anthropocentric or impersonal universe, and about animism as opposed to impersonal causality.

The idea that human fortune and misfortune are the result of random and impersonal events is totally counterintuitive, as humans naturally find meaning in imaginary sequences of design, intention, purpose, reward, and punishment. The subversive idea of creation and metamorphosis without any consciousness being involved has been correctly judged as tolling the bell for all animism.

Evolution, as the ruling paradigm in biology, has become the most potent symbol of de-animized science. The evolution paradigm is directly connected to the significant achievements of biology, the technological progress of biomedicine, and the idea of biological continuity. If humans arrived on earth through special creation, how is it possible that basic research in human biomedicine is carried out on mice, rats, hamsters, or dogs?

Scientists are perceived as altruistic when saving lives through research, but malevolent when their work is judged to threaten Christianity and morality. Public ambivalence about "science" is tied to those added features that seem to be attached to scientific expertise, in the form of generalized skepticism and universalism. For many believers, and not only Christians, there is an analogy between an order of nature, designed by a deity, and the moral order, which keeps social chaos at bay. A rejection of the idea of design in nature implies a rejection not only of social traditions, but of morality itself. A direct challenge to Genesis is seen as destroying a moral community.[22] Belief in special creation is tied not only to the idea that humans are morally superior, but also to salvation. For Christians, creation and redemption are inextricably tied,[23] and so evolution becomes a direct assault on the foundation to the moral drama of sin and salvation.

In 1924, William Jennings Bryan said: "All the ills from which America suffers can be traced back to the teaching of evolution. It would be better to destroy every other book ever written, and save just the first three verses of Genesis."[24] And Bryan's ideas are still alive and well among American politicians. After the massacre in Columbine High School in Colorado in April 1999, Representative Tom DeLay, then the House majority whip, put the blame on the teaching of children "that they are nothing but glorified apes who are evolutionized out of some primordial soup of mud."[25]

The Ambivalent Triumph of Science

In 2006, a representative sample of the United States adult population was asked to rank the prestige of various occupations, and the results are fairly encouraging for those who are concerned about the public image of science (see *Figure 7-1*). Six occupations are perceived to have "very great" prestige by at least half of all adults—firefighters (63%), doctors (58%), nurses (55%), scientists (54%), teachers (52%) and military officers (51%). They are followed by police officers (43%) and clergy (40%). It should be noted that since 1977, scientists have fallen 12 points, from 66% to 54%, but this has been true of all occupations, with teachers being the only exception.

This survey proves that popular fantasies about scientists are quite positive; Americans perceive scientists as serving others at the expense of their own welfare. "Scientist" is rated close to those occupations that regularly strive to save lives, regardless of risk and effort. Firefighters, the military, and the police regularly put their lives on the line. Medical workers are expected to tend to the sick even when it puts them at risk. Scientists are apparently imagined as tied to the success of biomedicine, because most Americans are aware of how much we owe to life-saving technology developed thanks to scientific research.[26]

What becomes clear is that respondents rated occupations on a selflessness scale, with those viewed as heroic and altruistic at the top and those viewed as selfish and materialistic at the bottom. Starting with "Member of Congress," we see thirteen occupations that are held in some contempt. At the bottom are business executives, real-estate agents, and stockbrokers, all tainted by their association with profit. In the land of unfettered capitalism, this scale reflects a real yearning for honest work and a society where farmers and engineers, who produce tangible goods, have higher status than stockbrokers.

Teachers are held in higher esteem than clergy, and this is a clear reflection of secularization. Education is tied to science, and the teacher is the local representative of the secular science-knowledge complex. The prestige survey asked about "scientist," and this brings to mind an image of a person possibly at

Figure 7-1
Prestige of 23 Professions and Occupations[27]

	Very Great Prestige	Considerable Prestige	Some Prestige	Hardly Any Prestige At All	Not Sure/ Refused
	%	%	%	%	%
Firefighter	63	23	11	3	-
Doctor	58	30	10	1	1
Nurse	55	24	17	4	-
Scientist	54	26	15	4	*
Teacher	52	22	20	6	*
Military officer	51	30	16	3	1
Police officer	43	26	26	4	1
Priest/Minister/Clergyman	40	28	24	7	1
Farmer	36	21	26	15	1
Engineer	34	35	26	4	1
Member of Congress	28	23	31	17	1
Architect	27	24	33	19	1
Athlete	23	24	33	19	1
Lawyer	21	23	36	20	*
Entertainer	18	23	37	22	*
Accountant	17	30	40	11	1
Banker	17	29	43	11	1
Journalist	16	27	41	16	*
Union Leader	12	21	38	25	3
Actor	12	13	37	37	1
Business executive	11	30	43	15	1
Stockbroker	11	25	42	22	1
Real estate agent/broker	6	17	44	32	1

work in the lab. The abstract term "science" brings to mind power over nature and over human life and death. "Science" always brings to mind the powerful, inaccessible natural sciences.[28] We cannot really fathom what happens in a real lab, but we can read about the powerful people there in *The New Men* by C.P. Snow and in *Kantor's Dilemma*, by Carl Djerassi. The human sciences, seemingly more accessible, and much less powerful, inspire little respect. Those laboring in them are often imagined as weak, deviant, pathetic, or even tragic, to judge by their portraits in such novels as *Pnin*, by Vladimir Nabokov, *Herzog*, by Saul Bellow, *On Beauty*, by Zadie Smith, or *Point of No Return*, by J.P. Marquand.

The triumph of science has always been regarded with real ambivalence, which was part of the early critiques of modernity. Science and its promoters have been perceived as powerful but forbidding, and they inspired both admiration and fear. Balzac's *La Peau de Chagrin*, published in 1831, describes the nascent world of academic research. Reading that novel, we realize that the conceptual structure of academic research was well in place even then. Balzac satirizes natural scientists of that period, and we can see not only that naturalism was well in place, but we also see the popular image of the scientist as odd and out of touch with everyday reality, while at the same time in total mastery of a field of research. Scientists are described as eccentric, ascetic, aloof, and strange, but awe-inspiring because of their intelligence and their total commitment to studying a particular segment of nature. *La Peau de Chagrin* describes not only the "hard" sciences of physics and chemistry, but also the beginnings of the behavioral sciences, as its characters discuss collecting statistics on the personality of gamblers or the effects of body chemistry on behavior. These ideas, current then as well as today, are treated with ambivalent skepticism. In *Madame Bovary* (1857), Gustave Flaubert describes "Science" as heartless and vain through the image of the pharmacist M. Homais, the spokesman for Enlightenment and Progress.

Warm Religion and Cold Science

Science is, in principle, democratic and open; it is a matter of publicly accessible texts. In practice, however, it is quite esoteric. You need more than ambition and a high IQ to get a Ph.D. or to publish anything of substance in any academic field. To achieve any kind of true membership in a scientific fraternity (and it is usually a fraternity, a masculine territory), you run the gauntlet of peer review, and engage in constant exchanges characterized by innovation, contention, competition, criticism, and even contempt. Academics are independent, contentious, counterdependent, antiauthoritarian, and often contemptuous of claims they consider unfounded. There is plenty of contention in religion, of course, but it is managed very differently, through reliance on tradition, authority, revelation, and violence.

To appreciate the fine points of an article published in chemistry, or in linguistics, takes much training—which is rarely acquired by self-teaching. This is easily demonstrated when an accomplished academic tries to read a published article outside his/her field. A neglibible percentage of humanity is capable of understanding relativity theory or Maxwell's equations. Even when it comes to "softer" fields such as historical research on the popes in Avignon or laboratory manipulation in social psychology, a real understanding of academic research is simply beyond the reach of the uninitiated. In a very real sense, the majority of humanity is excluded from science. A tiny minority keeps the science discourse going by devoting enormous energy to it, while the majority finds it inaccessible and incoherent.

Religious believers don't think in terms of animism, naturalism, or theoretical abstractions. They are attached to stories they learned as children, and to sacred traditions that hold their world together. Unlike academic discourse, the religious message is accessible to all, and does not require intellectual effort or formal training. That is why it can be learned at such an early age. Parents share with very young children religious ideas that the latter gobble up without any difficulty. Scientists do not share with young children our tentative theories of black holes or the making of the French Revolution. At any age and with any training, we are all invited to pass judgment (and it better be positive) on religious claims, but no one is asking us for our opinion on the claims of organic chemistry. Everybody is invited to embrace the good news of religion, but very few are asked to think about the interactions of carbon with oxygen. Religious cosmology is accessible and attractive to all humans, including children, and can be taught informally by any illiterate mother anywhere in the world. The cosmology of modern physics will remain impenetrable to 99.999% of humanity forever.[29]

Every religion offers us a comprehensive, coherent, convincing, simple, accessible, and pleasing theory of the universe and our place in it. The narratives of molecular biology cannot compete with those of world religions. Science is cold, distant, strong, and offers no emotional gratification, while religion is warm and consoling.[30] What generic science offers us is a series of complicated, disputed, and tentative claims that are inaccessible to most of humanity. Science will forever remain inaccessible, and cannot compete with accessible and attractive religious stories. Most science narratives are inaccessible, and even when we can follow them, they offer us no moral dramas or moral victories. Still, the power of science has captivated most religionists, or so it seems.

Appropriating Science

What the image of science has been stimulating—in the private and public imaginations—are mostly fantasies of power and superiority. Over the past two centuries, there have been numerous examples of religionists feeling a strong need to obtain legitimacy from the power of the new social institution that rose in prestige above revelation. The rising authority of science has led religionists to claim it in the most direct and magical way. Since the 19th century, we have seen the founding of hundreds of religious movements, using the term "science" in their official names and claiming a unity of science and religion.

The best known is the "healing" movement of Christian Science, founded in 1879 by Mary Baker Eddy (1821-1910) and originally called the First Church of Christ, Scientist (immortalized by Nathanael West as the First Church of Christ, Dentist [31]). Eddy's ideas were totally animistic, of course, and the science label reflected her magical thinking about the power of words and the desire to appear powerful.[32] Christian Science was followed by Divine Science, Religious Science, and Jewish Science. A little-known early version of African-American pseudo-Islam was founded in Newark, New Jersey, in 1913, as the Moorish Science Temple of America.[33] The magical gesture of using the term "science" had little effect on the fortunes of these movements.

More recently, the cultural standing of science has led religionists to claim that their cosmology should be labeled science, demonstrating again the loss of power that was once ascribed to revelation. It is the victory of "science" and secularization that leads fundamentalists to offer us first "Creation science" and an "Institute for Creation Research," and then "Intelligent Design." All of these rather desperate attempts merely serve to remind us that religious tradition has been losing its authority.

There have been several movements that expressed the desire to grab the mantle of science in the defense of generic animism. The modern movement to establish "scientifically" the existence of the human soul is a case in point. This started in the heyday of spiritualism, and led to the founding of the Society for Psychical Research in London in 1882. The Society, led by such luminaries as Henri Bergson, William James, and Arthur James Balfour, was energized by the dreams of some 19th-century intellectuals, who were seeking physical evidence for the existence of the soul through the investigation of "psychics" and "paranormal" events. This elite version of spiritualism in turn brought about the development of "parapsychology" in the United States.[34]

The enormous prestige of modern physics has created a minor industry of authors who attempt to use its arcane theories in defense of religion. For a century now, religious apologists have been using the concepts of modern physics—such as relativity, the uncertainty principle, and quantum mechanics—in hundreds of books and articles. These are concepts very few of us, except for those with a Ph.D. in physics, could begin to decipher. Religious apologists invoke these to impress non-experts, and to prove how much (imagined) physics has become a source of knowledge and authority, and how the prestige of (imagined) science has surpassed that of (experienced and lived) religion. But some attempts to prove the truth of religion are close to believers' everyday dreams.

In a 2003 *Newsweek* poll, "…84% of Americans said prayers for others can have a positive effect on their recovery, and 74% said that would be true even if they didn't know the patient."[35] Moreover, 72% thought "…that praying to God can cure someone even if science says the person doesn't stand a chance."[36] Matching this expression of faith, unmatched elsewhere in the First World, a research program has been carried out over the past two decades, with millions of dollars being spent on studying the efficacy of prayer with various medical problems.

One of the many absurdities of prayer efficacy research is its ecumenicity. Prayers coming from all religions are considered equally useful and included in one study. This reflects a praiseworthy spirit of multiculturalism, but is actually totally divorced from the actions of real believers as they pray and consider their faith to be superior to those of others. At least one of the recent "miracle" studies has been exposed as a fraud,[37] and the results of the whole enterprise are expectedly pathetic.[38] What the researchers obviously don't know is that the last word on the subject (i.e., prayer has no effect) was said already in 1872.[39]

Historically, the same Protestant milieu has given rise to the so-called "Biblical archeology" movement, which has attempted to corroborate the claims made in Biblical narratives. This movement was started and led by William Foxwell Albright and his disciple, Nelson Glueck. Albright declared that his findings had shown the books of Genesis and Exodus to be truly historical accounts. Dr. Glueck spent his time in the 1950s providing accurate locations for every miraculous event reported in those books, including the Binding of Isaac.[40] Fifty years later, this triumphalist effort is totally ignored.

Ivory Tower Revolutions

The continuing changes in academia in the 20th century were not limited to the curriculum, where those changes reflected the triumph of the modern elite. There were cultural changes in the 1960s and 1970s, decades that witnessed a general revolution in campus life. It is hard to recall that most institutions of higher education used to be segregated, all male, with some degree of visible religious affiliation, and with an *in loco parentis* policy. Starting in the 1960s, U.S. campuses went through an antiauthoritarian revolution, which can be criticized with hindsight as being limited to "lifestyle" issues, but which, at the same time, had an enormous social impact. Some of the changes had to do with the emancipation of undergraduates, the coming of feminism, ethnic diversity, and sexuality. What is often overlooked is that this revolution, which had so much of the Enlightenment spirit in it, was also about secularization. And this accelerated secularization in higher education paralleled the same process in public schools all over the country, as prayers and Bible readings were disappearing. Changes in the ethnic composition of students and then faculty have been a major factor in the secularization, or to be exact de-Christianization, of elite institutions.[41]

One symbolic issue, which has been almost forgotten, was the old custom of mandatory chapel attendance, which was in effect even in many public universities in the late 19th century, and was in the process of being eliminated by the middle of the 20th. We should recall that compulsory chapel at Princeton University ended in 1964. At Brown University, it ended for men in 1959 but for women only in 1968. These events in the 1960s were the result of long-term processes, and we know that compulsory chapel attendance had already ended on most campuses in the 1950s. The mid-century decade is often described as a time of religious revival, but obviously there was still movement in the other direction. It took a Supreme Court decision[42] in 1972 to end mandatory chapel attendance in the United States for uniformed services academies. The old argument that chapel attendance was instrumental in building character was rejected by the Supreme Court.

The 1960s changes in the culture of the campuses had an enormous impact on society. Both Lipset[43] and Hofstadter[44] underlined the gap between the campus culture, led by radical faculty, and the rest of society, but we can observe much narrowing of that gap. The hundreds of Ivory Tower campuses all over the country have not just been isolated islands of secularity and Enlightenment; they have been a source of massive influence through many millions of students.

The extent of secularization in higher education is something that we often fail to appreciate. It meant not only that public colleges and universities eliminated any residue of religious content in their curriculum or in campus life, but that over the past century, and more so during the past half-century, hundreds of denominational colleges and universities, affiliated with various Christian denominations, have become either completely secular or minimally religious. (Does anybody even know that the American Baptist Convention considered the University of Chicago an affiliated institution until 1960?)

What the process was about was not only the shedding of religious ties, but a clear trade-off between denominational affiliation and academic standards.[45] Any kind of denominational tie, even the most minimal, still means a diminished reputation, and those institutions that became totally secular experienced a total remaking of academic culture. Many denominational colleges and universities that have kept their nominal religious affiliation are totally different today from what they were 50 years ago. It will suffice to mention such institutions as Notre Dame, Fordham, and Boston College to illustrate that.

Threats to Naturalism

Academic research must have epistemic authority to survive, and it does with societal recognition, which rests on the assumption that its practitioners possess expertise unavailable to others. Popular support for alternative claims about humanity and the universe are a threat to epistemic authority. Should we take a stand against animism? Animistic beliefs have survived and are doing well everywhere. In some well known cases, popular beliefs reflect a rejection of naturalism, but the problem is more complex, because in other cases popular belief systems are justified, if needed, with the help of naturalist ideas.

Alan Leshner, chief executive officer of the American Association for the Advancement of Science identified the gap between the U.S. public and science as "an uncertain understanding—at best—of what science is and is not."[46] To illustrate that, he noted that 60% of Americans believe in "extrasensory perception," 40% believe astrology is a science, and 47% do not believe that humans evolved from lower species.

It is not just animistic schemas that constitute what we will consider invalid and ignorant ideas. Astrology, in its many forms, is popular everywhere, and not only in the United States. It is (and will always be) much more popular than astrophysics. It flourishes in every modern society, because it is accessible and uses natural language.[47] In 1975 and again in 1986, the American Humanist Association published statements against astrology signed by prominent academic researchers and intellectuals.[48] This move was criticized by Feyerabend[49] as an attempt to use authority rather than evidence, and beyond that, it has hardly been noticed. It has had no impact on the burgeoning global business of astrology.

How is the belief in creation different from the belief in astrology, which originally reflected geocentric and anthropocentric fantasies, just like religion? Astrology today involves little investment of resources, and is consumed only privately. It is not tied to identity, and its Western proponents will often use non-animistic explanations in its defense. Similarly, most believers in "extrasensory perception" will offer naturalist theories in its support, despite its historical origins in 19th-century spiritualism. This is another triumph for modernity and secularization, and another ignominious defeat for animism. What started with belief in the human soul in the case of "extrasensory perception," and with the idea of consciousness in the planets in the case of astrology must now rely on (unconvincing) naturalist arguments. Animism, except in its institutionalized form, as religion, must go into hiding.

The main difference between most forms "non-science" and religion is that followers of astrology don't organize to challenge astrophysics. Followers of some religions sometimes do that, and at this level, the prevalence of animism is a threat. Religion could be a threat to academic research only in those cases where particular religious traditions have enough political power to challenge academia.

The more general challenge to academia is that, as we observe the world from the ivory tower, we find a real gap in knowledge between the academic experts and the masses in every field. Pedantic professors tear out their thinning hair in despair when they encounter the limited or false notions of the less educated about anything from history to physics. Should we mobilize our forces to fight ignorance, or can we leave the masses in their philistinism? To teach the masses how to tell "science" from "non-science," as Leshner suggested, means developing critical thinking, and this is what education and science education are all about.

The American Way

The academic world has been identified with secularity for several good reasons:

- At the most abstract level, institutionalized naturalism must collide with animism. It is axiomatic that the strategies of animism and naturalism will be in psychological and epistemological conflict.

- The academy has been created through the secularization of culture.

- The secularity of academic researchers means a total rejection of religious authority.

- Specific theories in biology, astrophysics, and geology, as well as historical research, challenge specific religious doctrines.

- The academic ethos, which is anti-authoritarian, challenges all outside powers.

- The process of secularization in academia has not stopped.

Hofstadter's historical framing shows that what looks today like a gap between the elite and the masses is just one moment in a long process of secularizing American public education from the top down. What is significant about the long-range historical change is what can rightly be called a trickle-down effect. There is always a gap between the academic elite and the rest of society, but the real change follows elite leadership.

When it comes to religion and public life, the United States has always had a unique way, as de Tocqueville noted.[50] Public discourse about religion in the U.S. has always been generic, to avoid the violent conflicts that used to characterize inter-religious rivalries elsewhere.[51] This generic discourse in turn created a unique type of secularization. The 34th President, Dwight D. Eisenhower, expressed his creed as follows: "Our government makes no sense, unless it is founded on a deeply felt religious faith—and I don't care what it is."[52] This ecumenical show of faith, often cited to demonstrate the centrality of religion in U.S. culture, paradoxically reflects the extent of secularization, which in the 20th century allowed only such generic expressions.

Animism and narcissism will never go away. The psychological factors leading to the human attachment to animism are universal, but are expressed in different cultural-historical settings. Americans, to use Freud's term, are no more narcissistic than Europeans, but the course of the American Enlightenment has been unique. In most of the Western world, animism and naturalism can easily coexist while compartmentalized, because animism has been privatized, and naturalism institutionalized in education and research. In the U.S., animism is still public and institutionalized, and what we observe is a failure to compartmentalize, together with the secularization of education at all levels, supported by the great historical tradition of avoiding religious conflict. We discover that the great American paradox is the onward march of secularization, which can no longer be hidden, at the center of cultural production.

ENDNOTES

1. S. Freud, "Introductory Lectures on Psychoanalysis," in *The Standard Edition of the Complete Psychological Work of Sigmund Freud*, vol. 16 (London: The Hogarth Press), 243-476.

2. A.F.C. Wallace, *Religion: An Anthropological View* (New York: Random House, 1966), 52.

3. M. Argyle and B. Beit-Hallahmi, *The Social Psychology of Religion* (London: Routledge & Kegan Paul, 1975); Beit-Hallahmi, *Prolegomena to The Psychological Study of Religion.* (Lewisburg, PA: Bucknell University Press, 1989); Beit-Hallahmi and Argyle, *The Psychology of Religious Behaviour, Belief and Experience* (London: Routledge, 1997).

4. A. Cromer, *Uncommon Sense: The Heretical Nature of Science* (New York: Oxford University Press, 1993); L. Wolpert, *The Unnatural Nature of Science* (Cambridge, MA: Harvard University Press, 2000).

5. J.G Frazer, *The Golden Bough* (New York: Macmillan, 1951), 633.

6. G.W Graffin and W.B. Provine, "The Most Eminent Evolutionary Scientists have Surprising Views on how Religion Relates to Evolution," (2006) http://www.americanscientist.org/template/AssetDetail/assetid/55593/page/2/?&print=yes.

7. R.K. Merton, "The Normative Structure of Science," in *The Sociology of Science*, ed. R.K. Merton (Chicago: University of Chicago Press, 1973).

8. D.A. Hollinger, *Science, Jews, and Secular Culture: Studies in Mid-Twentieth Century American Intellectual History* (Princeton: Princeton University Press, 1996).

9. B. Eiduson, *Scientists: Their Psychological World* (New York: Basic Books, 1962); Eiduson and L. Beckman, eds., *Science as a Career Choice: Theoretical and Empirical Studies* (New York: The Russell Sage Foundation, 1973); G.J. Feist, *The Psychology of Science and the Origins of the Scientific Mind* (New Haven: Yale University Press, 2006); A. Roe, *The Making of a Scientist* (New York: Dodd, Mea, 1952).

10. Ostling R.N., (2005). Huston Smith, famed scholar on world religions, focuses anew on his own faith of Christianity. Associated Press, September 22.

11. R. Hofstadter, *Anti-Intellectualism in American Life* (New York: Knopf. 1963), 125-126.

12. See Hollinger, 1996; G.M. Marsden, *The Soul of the American University: From Protestant Establishment to Established Nonbelief* (New York: Oxford University Press, 1996); *The Secular Revolution: Power, Interests, and Conflict in the Secularization of American Public Life*, C. Smith, ed. (Berkeley: University of California Press, 2003); A.D. White, *A History of the Warfare of Science with Theology in Christendom* (Buffalo, NY: Prometheus Books, 1993).

13. See Hofstadter, 1963.

14. *Engel v. Vitale* (1962).

15. *Abington School District v. Schempp* (1963).

16. K.D. Wald, *Religion and Politics in the United States*, 4th ed. (Lanham, MD: Rowman and Littlefield Publishers, 2003).

17. *McLean v. Arkansas Board of Education* (1982).

18. *Kitzmiller et al. v. Dover Area School District* (2005).

19. A. Coulter, *Godless: The Church of Liberalism* (New York: Crown Forum, 2006).

20. Cf. Miller and Pennock, Chapter 1.

21. A. Lewis, "Abroad at Home: Something Rich and Strange," *The New York Times*, October 12, 1999.

22. E. Durkheim, *The Elementary Forms of the Religious Life* (New York: Free Press, 1965).

23. S. Hauerwas, *With the Grain of the Universe: The Church's Witness and Natural Theology* (Grand Rapids, MI: Bazos Press, 2001).

24. See Hofstadter, *Anti-Intellectualism in American Life*, 125.

25. Lewis, "Abroad at Home: Something Rich and Strange," *The New York Times*. October 12, 1999.

26. Cf. C.P. Snow, *Two Cultures and the Scientific Revolution* (Cambridge: Cambridge University Press, 1965).

27. Harris Poll #58, July 26, 2006. See http://www.harrisinteractive.com/harris_poll/index.asp?PID=685.

28. See Hollinger, 1996.

29. E.g. *Dark Matter in Cosmology, Clocks and Test of Fundamental Laws,* B. Guiderdoni, G. Greene, D. Hinds, and J. Tran Tranh Van, eds. (Gif-sur-Yvette: Edition Frontieres, 1995).

30. J. Monod, *Chance and Necessity* (London: Collins, 1970).

31. N. West, *Miss Lonelyhearts* (New York: Avon, 1933).

32. H. Bloom, *The American Religion: The Making of a Post-Christian Nation* (New York: Simon & Schuster, 1992).

33. A.H. Fauset, *Black Gods of the Metropolis* (Philadelphia: University of Pennsylvania Press, 1944).

34. S. H. Mauskopf and M. McVaugh, *The Elusive Science: Origins of Experimental Psychical Research* (Baltimore: Johns Hopkins University Press, 1980); R. L. Moore, *In Search of White Crows: Spiritualism, Parapsychology, and American Culture* (New York: Oxford University Press, 1977).

35. C. Kalb, "Faith & Healing," *Newsweek,* November 17, 2003, 47-55, 54.

36. Ibid., 48.

37. K.Y Cha, D.P. Wirth and R.A. Lobo, "Does Prayer Influence the Success of In Vitro Fertilization-embryo Transfer?" *Journal of Reproductive Medicine,* 46 (2001): 781-787.

38. B. Carey, "Long-awaited Medical Study Questions the Power of Prayer," *The New York Times,* March 31, 2006; R.P Sloan, *Blind Faith: The Unholy Alliance of Religion and Medicine* (New York: St. Martin's Press, 2006); Sloan and R. Ramakrishnan, "Science, Medicine, and Intercessory Prayer," *Perspectives in Biology and Medicine,* 49 (2006): 504-514.

39. F. Galton, "Statistical Inquiries into the Efficacy of Prayer," *Fortnightly Review,* 12 (1872): 125-135.

40. N. Glueck, *Rivers in the Desert: A History of the Negev* (New York: W. W. Norton, 1968).

41. Hollinger, *Science, Jews, and Secular Culture: Studies in Mid-Twentieth Century American Intellectual History.*

42. *Anderson v. Laird,* 1972.

43. S.M. Lipset, "The Academic Mind at the Top: The Political Behavior and Values of Faculty Elites," *Public Opinion Quarterly,* 46 (1982): 143-168.

44. See Hofstadter, 1963.

45. Burtchaell, J.T. (1998). *Dying of the Light: The Disengagement of Colleges and Universities from their Christian Churches.* Grand Rapids: Wm. B. Eerdmans.

46. M. Moran, "Science Can't Thrive in Ivory Tower," *Psychiatric News* (July 6, 2007): 24. http://pn.psychiatryonline.org/cgi/content/full/42/13/24.

47. Cf. T.W. Adorno, "The Stars Down to Earth," *The Los Angeles Times* astrology column, *Telos,* 19 (1974): 13-90.

48. http://www.americanhumanist.org/about/astrology.html.

49. Feyerabend, *Science in a Free Society* (London: Verso, 1982).

50. De Tocqueville, *Democracy in America* (1835).

51. S.M. Lipset, *The First New Nation: The United States in Historical and Comparative Perspective* (New York: Basic Books, 1963).

52. Hofstadter, *Anti-Intellectualism in American Life* (New York: Knopf, 1963), 84.

8. Toward a Clear Frontier between Science and Religion in Education

Juan Antonio Aguilera Mochón

The longstanding science-religion conflict continues to be a highly topical subject—for two reasons especially. First, advances in science and technology often force religion to revise old opinions and adopt new ones. And second, education is an arena in which science and religion may conflict. (And it will likely remain so.)

My intention here is not to review the science-religion conflicts, but rather to clarify the roots of these conflicts, and provide some tools to facilitate the delimitation of scientific and religious competences. Additionally, I shall offer some thoughts on how the above-mentioned situation can affect children's education.

Finally, I will describe the current science-religion conflict in Spanish schools, where religion is part of the curriculum. The particular religion of reference is Catholicism, although I think that the example of Spanish schools applies to all situations in which religion is taught alongside science as part of the general curriculum.

Toward the Root of the Conflict: Philosophical Presuppositions of Science and Religion

Defining religion and science—the scope and characteristics of each—is difficult and complex. Since there is little agreement among philosophers and other thinkers on the subject, I shall focus on delimiting a clear frontier between science and religion with respect to issues of direct educational interest. In an outstanding article, Martin Mahner and Mario Bunge[1] approached the epistemological roots of the possible conflicts between science and religion by establishing some basic philosophical premises that seem widely agreed upon. To

137

understand the conflict between science and religion, we must first understand these philosophical (and generally tacit, not explicit) presuppositions and the origin of the diverse modalities of the science-religion relationship.[2]

Philosophical Presuppositions of the Science

Science rests upon several core philosophical presuppositions. These include the belief that a reality exists (ontological realism); the belief that we can know that reality (gnoseologic realism); the idea that some propositions are about facts, and they are true in some measure (semantic realism); and the belief that the observable events in nature can only be explained by natural causes (methodological naturalism).

The methodological aspect of science is, of course, essential, and has been validated thousands of times in books and articles by philosophers of science. Yet with regard to methodological naturalism, I disagree with Mahner and Bunge,[3] who assure us that science assumes not only methodological, but *ontological* naturalism. In contrast, I think that in principle science cannot exclude the reality of unnatural (or supernatural) beings. On the other hand, I believe that we must clarify the limits of science's philosophical premises. Although this issue is very controversial, there is extensive agreement that science cannot make aesthetic valuations or moral statements. Science can *study* the artistic and the moral, but it cannot be "contrary" to them. Therefore, no "conflict" should exist in such areas (but more on this later).

Is science, then, unaware of, or external to, morality and "values"? This question usually causes confusion, for often the absence of a normative capacity in science is interpreted as an absence of values. But if we think deeply about this, we will see that some internal rules, and some very restrictive rules, do exist, and that some are moral rules. Where do these rules originate? The short answer is that science does not offer a morality but works with what Mahner and Bunge[4] characterize as a system of "internal values" (endoaxiology).

The "Internal Values" of Science

Science has internal values, which Mahner and Bunge highlight in their article. Those values include exactness, systemicity, and logical consistency (i.e., logical values); definiteness, also known as clarity, and maximal truth, also known as adequacy of ideas to facts (i.e., semantical values); testability and the possibility of scrutinizing and justifying the very methods employed to test ideas (i.e., methodological values); and, finally, critical thinking, open-mindedness (but not blank-mindedness), veracity, and giving credit where credit is due. These are attitudinal and moral values.

I find this list eminently sensible, but somewhat brief. Some important values are missing because it seems to me, there is no desire for completeness in Mahner and Bunge's enumeration. Thus we can add the following:

- Simplicity, explanatory power (i.e., logical values).
- Objectivity, creativity, self-correction (i.e., methodological values).

Still other values are missing because they are so taken for granted in the scientific field that they are almost invisible. These include freedom of thought, freedom of expression, and non-violence—that is, attitudinal and moral values.

I will elucidate the importance of these aspects of attitudinal and moral values to science. But first, one wonders just how significant these values are in the world outside science. These values are especially linked to what, in the modern world, we usually consider the most precious and specifically human values: critical thinking, freedom of thought, and freedom of expression. These are different "values," but they are closely interrelated. They are what make us free, make us responsible, and make us human. Along with non-violence, they are values that everyone hurries to proclaim nowadays; but they are rarely sustained or sincerely promoted. I think these free thought values are assumed to be part of science—as part of the scientific method—much more than in other areas of life, although we find those freedoms undermined by the natural anti-libertarian trends of certain authoritarian scientists themselves. In short, critical reason and the internal values of science in general can be the best weapons against the new forms of domination and manipulation in society.

Finally, it is clear from the philosophical presuppositions proposed that the internal values of science do not admit any kind of faith as an explanation, and do not consider any truth as immutable. In other words, the scientific methods and scientific results are secular and independent of religious beliefs.[5]

Philosophical Presuppositions of Religion

Religion, too, rests upon several main philosophical assumptions. These are the belief that a reality exists (i.e., ontological realism); a belief that that reality is knowable (i.e., gnoseological realism); and the belief that there are supernatural beings and facts (i.e., ontological supernaturalism).

Clearly, the fundamental difference between religion and science is the (religious) belief in supernaturalism. It is also clear that the methodological difference occurs at the point of obtaining knowledge about how the world is, and how it works. The "religious methodology" can be characterized by this so-called connection with the supernatural. This connection is considered the essential source of knowledge, and includes revelation (which contains sacred scriptures and appearances), tradition, authority, intuition, contemplation, meditation and prayer. In practice, this methodology gives rise to differentiation, owing to very different traditions and experiences in connection with the supernatural. The fact that religious "truths" can not be verified, corrected, or modified means that the practices of some faiths are often radically incompatible with other faiths.

The System of "External Values" (Exoaxiology) of the Religion

In contrast to science, religion posits a system of external values. Religion makes value judgments—judgments that affect natural objects. I will not discuss the broad field of religious values. What is worth mentioning here is that some of the "internal values" (endoaxiology) that characterize science are barely discernable in religion. This can be illustrated by some significant examples of qualities present—and absent—from religion (at the end of the article I will specify the possible confrontations of major educative relevance):

> Self-correction (which entails doubt, provisionality): In principle, these features are excluded specifically from the religious realm. For example, it is believed that the word of God written in the holy books expresses unimpeachable truths. In practice, we know that religions are forced to change, to adapt to new times and to new knowledge (brought by science, usually).

> Systematicity, logic, clarity of language: Due to one characteristic—the concept of "mystery"—all those features fade. Generally, logical and rational thinking is subordinated to faith and to the dogmatic truths transmitted by the sacred texts and the religious authorities.

> Unicity: While there are no differences among scientific disciplines regarding reasons of belief or other ideological premises, there is a multitude of religions that are basically incompatible due to mutually exclusive doctrines. Generally, there is little possibility of agreement (it is rarely tried) among different religious doctrines even though they appear to outside observers to have minor differences.

Now that we know the philosophical presuppositions that can help clarify the differences between the field of science and the field of religion, we can recognize the possible areas of conflict. And we can move forward in the process of delimitating the frontiers between the scientific and the religious.

In Search of a Precise Delimitation of Frontiers

Searching for a neat frontier, we must know what religion says about science—and vice-versa. Of course, in order to do this succinctly, I must again summarize extraordinarily.

What Does Religion Say about Science?

I wish to highlight, in this section, the fact that science has achieved remarkable success in understanding and explaining the natural world. This has progressed to the point where today, most of the followers of the majority of religions in the West declare that the natural world is the proper domain of science.

What Does Science Say about Religious Beliefs?

Science usually does not enter into the content of religious beliefs (but see later), so here we are interested in knowing what *the sciences* say about those beliefs, and what scientists themselves believe. In this respect, the most relevant data were obtained in surveys carried out last century by Leuba[6] and Larson and Witham.[7] They reported that the higher the status of the scientists, the less likely they were to believe in a personal God or in life after death. On the other hand, however, most scientists *declare* that science does not conflict with religion. They manifest an enormous respect for religious beliefs, but without ever specifying what these beliefs actually are. We have an example of this in Stephen Jay Gould's celebrated book, *Rock of Ages*.[8] Gould emphasizes the "non conflict" between, and the separation of, scientific and religious "magisteria"; but he does so without ever stopping to consider what we might call "strong" religious assertions about the operation of the natural world, e.g., supernatural interventions in the operation of this world.

This evasive attitude avoids the points of potential conflict, but it is not very useful because it only postpones the resolution of possible problems. For this reason, I believe that, from the point of view of science, it is necessary to move fearlessly ahead toward the delimitation of the scope of science versus religion.

The Scope of Science and Religion

Based on my earlier arguments, I believe that the vast majority of scientists and religious people would actually agree that claims regarding natural reality fall into the sphere of science. It is a key point. From it follows, logically, that religious claims about natural reality can be subjected to skeptical—i.e., scientific—doubt.

The key word is "can." Since although it "can" be done, almost nobody does it. (In my opinion, it is with the "can" that the "conflict escapists" usually fail.)

Speaking in ethical terms, can we say that science "must" evaluate any relevant assertion about the functioning of the natural world, and that therefore science "must" consider the relevant religious assertions about the natural world?

Whatever the answer is, it seems clear that science "should not" hide its conclusions about the natural world simply because these conclusions would upset some collective. To put it more starkly, science should not hold any "respect" for religious beliefs about natural reality.

This idea, this declaration of principles, is what allows us to continue towards delimitating the frontier from the scientific point of view. To accomplish this, we must continue to clarify and classify the assertions made from outside science. Is science able to say something about the truth of any assertion? We know when it is not—but when is it able, and are there degrees in the response capacity?

I will try now to offer a first classification (which is amenable improvement and expansion, of course) of the types of assertions that science faces. I will speak explicitly of statements of religious character, which is what concerns us here, but the classification could apply to any type of assertion.

The Character of (Religious) Assertions from the Scientific Point of View

I propose the following classification of statements from a scientific point of view:

1. Proven true and explained by science.

2. Not proven true, but compatible with science.

3. Proven true, but unexplained by science.

4. Unscientific (unverifiable/unfalsifiable, fictitious, without factual content, moral, aesthetic).

5. Proven false.

6. Scientifically false: not proven false, but not compatible with scientific knowledge.

7. Anti-scientific.

Of course, in each type there can be degrees, mainly in types 1 and 3. In fact, if we follow Popperian thinking, then any assertion cannot be assumed as definitively proven scientifically.

To clarify this incipient classification, I will illustrate it with real examples relating to the arena of human health. I shall also discuss some of the more outstanding possible sources of conflict:

1. Proven true and explained by science: "Patients for whom doctors have given up hope have recovered thanks to new medicines."

2. Not proven true, but compatible with science: "Some people terminally ill recovered after being touched by Jesus." (Jesus of the Gospels.)

3. Proven true, but unexplained by science: "Patients for whom the best doctors had given up hope have recovered."

4. Unscientific / Moral: "Patients exhibit exemplary behavior when the doctors had given up hope of their recovering."

5. Proven false: "Patients that the best doctors had given up hope for and then have recovered are all Christians."

6. Scientifically false: "Some people are raised from the dead."

7. Anti-scientific: "Patients for whom the best doctors had given up hope of recovery have recovered in a way that is and will be inexplicable scientifically."

In the proposed classification, the only type of assertions in which science has no competence is the unscientific (4). For example, in assertion 4, science has nothing to say once it has corroborated the facts. And there are many religious assertions that are unscientific, e.g., all moral norms and judgments. Science by itself cannot pass judgment about goodness or evil. Only if the terms are defined externally can science conclude that something concrete is one thing or another. It can decide if it is fit for a purpose, but it can't assess the moral quality of that purpose.

Regarding holy texts that depict fictitious or symbolic events, science cannot make judgments. Science does not have the authority to make moral judgments. However, it is essential for science to address any discussion where a believer supports an assertion *that he himself regards as factual.* One complication is that in a religious thesis (theological, for example), there are often mixed assertions of several types, so it is important to dissect the speech by sorting the assertions, and to ask the writer or speaker for relevant clarifications when necessary.

From the side of science, the main conflicts arise, obviously, with claims of types 3, 5, 6 and 7 (although type 5 should make the case trivial). Type 7 relates to miracles that clash with science in a radical way, by denying its competence within its own sphere: the natural world. When someone says, of a miracle, that "science is not able to explain it, nor *will it be* able to," the speaker is denying that science can know and explain aspects of the functioning natural world, a key assumption of science. Therefore, the affirmation of a miracle is essentially anti-scientific.

The stories of miracles can sometimes be considered unscientific (type 4); e.g., when they are "enlightening" stories without pretension to factual truth. But very often they are considered true, objective accounts of facts affecting the natural world and therefore confront scientific expertise.

Although religions claim that miracles are produced by "transcendent" beings outside of the material world, those claims become subject to science as soon as they enter the realm of physical reality. Science cannot absolve itself from studying the causes of the physical facts. They cannot fail to be physical! In other words, when the "transcendent" or "supernatural" beings act in the natural world, they cease to be transcendent or supernatural and fall within the sphere of science. If religion claims that a supernatural entity has performed a physical marvel, this marvel, and its cause, is subject to scientific analysis.

In the example of a scientifically false assertion (type 6), science may rule that assertion false with a high degree of probability. It's an assertion that lacks evidence, and contradicts scientific experience, laws and theories. Science never has absolute certainty, and it is often impossible to quantify this degree of probability. In spite of this lack of absolute certainty, science is not obligated to add to each factual or explanatory assertion, a clause of extreme caution and provisionality.[9]

On the other hand, we have rare cases of gravely ill people who—against staggering odds—recover. These rare cases—often called miracles—are not sufficiently explained by science (type 3), although that does not mean that it is unexplainable (type 7) or incompatible with science. Indeed, one hopes that science will eventually supply an explanation. There is a popular tendency to interpret some unexpected (or simply fortunate) facts as supernatural interventions. In these cases, the claim may belong in fact to type 7 and 1 assertions.

The characterization and classification proposed here can be applied to other controversial issues, such as Intelligent Design. As the Intelligent Design doctrine denies science its ability to explain the natural world through natural causes, it clearly falls into the anti-scientific Type 7 claim. Besides that, in this doctrine there are assertions of both the proven falsity (type 5) and scientifically false (type 6).

We can now conclude that the inevitable and radical conflict between science and religion occurs when science moves onto unscientific ground. This occurs when someone intends, on behalf of science, to dictate moral standards or ways of life.

Conflict is also inevitable when religion enters the scientific field particularly through claims concerning miracles. Here we would not only include the "minor" miracles but also those proclaimed by the religions as major acts of creation made by a supernatural entity: for example, the origins of life or the origins of humans.

To ignore this radical conflict, as Stephen Jay Gould and so many others have done, involves closing one's eyes to the obvious reality. Based on my previous arguments, I think that one cannot maintain scientific thought (knowledge, methods and philosophical premises) alongside a belief in miracles. Note that I do not speak of an incompatibility between science and all the aspects of religion, but only with its consideration of miracles (in a broad sense) as true, real facts.

Educational Implications

What are the educational implications of the arguments presented so far? Is it possible for schools to harmonize serious scientific education alongside religious indoctrination?

A scientific education should consider and encompass two aspects of science: content and methodology. This means it must not only demonstrate scientific results but also an understanding of how science works—the "scientific method." This is based on the internal values of science. An essential part of the method is the idea that dogmatic beliefs about how the world is and how the world works cannot be assumed. It is the opposite of blind faith. The scientific method is grounded in doubt and skepticism; it demands verifiability, falsity, and self-correction. It seems clear that the scientific method is the best tool that humankind has devised to prevent and correct common errors such as superstition and magic.

If there is essential agreement with the arguments made here, a religious instruction that inculcates belief in miracles is not compatible with a scientific education. If we accept that miracles such as resurrections, virgin births, and divine interventions are radically anti-scientific and fail to explain the origins of life, we cannot accept them as compatible with science.

On the other hand, it is obvious that education is more than just delivering knowledge. Among other things, it includes learning how to acquire reliable knowledge, a way to face life's reality. Science represents a way to face reality based on its own "internal values" and philosophical premises. However, one must remember that these values do not extend from science "outward." Because scientific values are not universally shared, they will continue to produce conflict. (At the same time, if scientific values are considered positive, then they cannot, at the same time, be considered equal to or inferior to any opposing values.)

In order to clarify and systematize, I will outline some possible pairs of antithetical values that are especially important for delineating positions in education. Each pair is composed of a creedal value (c.v.) and a scientific value (s.v.). For example, one pair of contrasting values is uncritical acceptance of beliefs (c.v.) versus provisionality and verifiability (s.v.). Another example is the principle of authority (c.v.) versus demand for evidence (s.v.). A third is the immutability of beliefs (c.v.) versus the willingness to rectify in view of new evidences (s.v.). A fourth is faith (c.v.) versus critical thinking (s.v.). And a final value-pair is the recourse to "mystery" to solve logical inconsistencies (c.v.) versus rationality, which entails logical consistency (s.v.).

Any system of beliefs can be evaluated to see whether it is closer to creedal values or to scientific values. Of course, every person should have the freedom to choose his or her own values. Although religion is characterized by its support for beliefs and dogmas, this does not mean that religion only appeals to faith and lacks critical thinking. However, in contrast to science, there are important occasions on which faith prevails over critical thinking, and, in general, in which creedal values prevail over scientific values.

It is interesting that when we talk of religious education, we are talking, in fact, about a range of very diverse possibilities that can be, and often are, mutually incompatible. It behoves us to must remember the extent to which religions clash with one another, both today and in the past.

Likewise, it is relevant to note the importance of educational decisions affecting the schooling of young children. This is a complex matter, but it seems obvious that in their exposure to descriptions of natural reality and to the tools used to grasp it, science and its method should have the hegemonic role from the beginning (while of course adapting educational methods to age). Science education must demand that children be specially protected against the inculcation (based on the authority and other methods of indoctrination) of false scientific or anti-scientific assertions.

The Situation in Spain

Finally, I would like to comment on the science-religion conflict in Spanish schools. Until now, in Spain, there have not been episodes of religious intervention in scientific matters of the type seen in recent decades in the U.S. For example, there has not been a Creationist movement against the study of evolution in Spain, nor has any group tried to promote Intelligent Design as an alternative to natural evolution.

However, the structure of education in Spain explains why there is so little intervention from the religious sphere. Spanish public schools are legally required to offer the subject of "Religion" using public funds. Nowadays, attendance at religion classes is voluntary, but it is predominantly Roman Catholic, and the vast majority of students choose to attend from an early age. As a result, many students take many more hours of Religion than, say, biology. Naturally, in these Religion classes there is freedom to explain and instil the Church's view of creation and its belief in miracles. Religious instructors, as religious people guided by religious authorities and theologians, very rarely admit that evolution was and is a purely natural process. Therefore, a conflict occurs within the school because of the existence of religion classes where the curriculum can invade the field of science. In the religious private schools, the great majority of which are Catholic, the weight of religion is (as one might expect) even greater, as is the "invasion" of the scientific arena.

Therefore, most Spanish children learn in school to make the two subjects and approaches compatible through a variety of ways of "double thinking." Scientific knowledge and scientific thinking exist alongside knowledge based on a religious ideology that is not only unscientific (which is not such a problem) but is, from the scientist's point of view, false and anti-scientific. I fear that this confusing situation is not unique to Spain; rather, it exists in any nation where children receive religious indoctrination and science education at the same time, in the same school.

Conclusion

Building on the basic philosophical presuppositions of science and religion, I have attempted to delimit the frontier between them. As a consequence, I have clearly identified areas where the conflict is inevitable. This delimitation and identification is essential from the educational and pedagogic point of view. In the author's opinion, an indoctrination that is based on faith and belief in miracles is incompatible with a scientific education that is based on weighing evidence and critical thinking.

ENDNOTES

1. M. Mahner and M. Bunge, "Is Religious Education Compatible with Science Education?" *Science & Education* 5 (1996): 101-123.

2. See, for example, Chapter 7 of C. Haynes and W. Nord, *Taking Religion Seriously Across the Curriculum* (Washington, DC: Association for Supervision and Curriculum Development, 1998).

3. Mahner and Bunge (1996), 103.

4. Ibid.

5.   T. Jayaraman, "On Science and Secularism," ftp://ftp.csrd.uiuc.edu/pub/misc/mehrotra/bits/jayaraman.ps.gz. (Based on a talk delivered at the VII State Conference of the Tamilnadu Science Forum in January 1993); B.A. Kosmin, "The Congruence between the Scientific and the Secular," Science Education & Secular Values—a Symposium (Special Supplement to Religion in the News, summer/fall 2007).

6.   J. H. Leuba, "Religious Beliefs of American Scientists," *Harper's Magazine* 169, 1934, 291-300.

7.   E.J. Larson and L. Witham, "Leading Scientists still Reject God," *Nature* 394 (1998): 313; S.J. Gould, *Rocks of Ages: Science and Religion in the Fullness of Life* (Ballantine Books, New York, 1999).

8.   For an illustration and more detailed presentation of this type of assertions, see J.A. Aguilera, "La Ciencia frente a las Creencias Religiosas," *Mientras Tanto* 95 (2005): 125-153.

Scientific Literacy and Public Policy

9. Why Can't Science Tell the Truth? Scientific Literacy in a Postmodern World

Jeffrey Burkhardt

Introduction

For decades, people in the Science Establishment have lamented the lack of scientific literacy among the American public. Their concern reached a tipping point in the early 1990s, when educators and organizations such as the American Association for the Advancement of Science (AAAS), the National Center for Educational Progress (NCEP), the National Academies of Science/ National Research Council (NAS/NRC), and the National Science Foundation (NSF) began concerted efforts to improve science literacy.[1] Despite some success, however, the Science Establishment still has concerns: Even though the percentage of degrees (BS, MS, and Ph.D.) in Science and Engineering has remained constant,[2] and even though, contrary to anecdotal evidence, foreign-born students[3] have not displaced U.S. citizens and resident aliens in most of the S&E programs in U.S. universities,[4] we are again talking about scientific literacy. Why does the Science Establishment believe that serious, ongoing efforts at promoting scientific literacy are once again necessary?

This chapter explores this issue by addressing three main questions: (1) What is "scientific literacy" and why is it considered important? (2) What are some of the current socio-cultural impediments to scientific literacy? and (3) Are there aspects of the sciences themselves that may have undermined, or that contradict, the aims of the scientific literacy movement?

I argue that the Science Establishment may have underestimated the socio-cultural impediments to scientific literacy. The problem is not that people lack scientific skills or knowledge (a problem that can be remedied through better education and communication). Rather, many people simply don't value the things the Science Establishment thinks they should value. While the Science

Establishment may cloak itself in the high-minded mantle of educating the public, it may also have political and ideological goals—namely, advancing its own cause in the "culture wars" over issues like the teaching of Creationism—and asserting itself in a postmodern society that devalues science or simply ignores it.

What is Scientific Literacy and Why is it Important?

The Science Establishment's concern with scientific literacy was originally based on several things. One was comparative test scores: U.S. fourth- and eighth-graders have placed 8th in science testing (behind Korea and Japan, among others) and 14th in math testing (behind Korea, Japan, and Russia). To some this raises a red flag, suggesting that American dominance in science and technology may be eroding;[5] that Americans' lack of scientific literacy will be a liability both economically (in the global marketplace) and politically; and even that America's status as a global superpower may be jeopardized.

Additionally,

> Many of the social and political issues that have come to the forefront in the past decade have a strong scientific component. Issues related to reproductive technologies, the environment, and energy, for example, require a scientifically literate population for wise decision making in the coming years…Scientific literacy is important throughout students' lives as they participate in public policy issues related to technology; as they stay current with advances in areas such as biotechnology, medicine, and space exploration; and especially as they enter an increasingly scientifically based workforce.[6]

In short, efforts to increase scientific literacy have a political and a practical component. Americans participate and compete in an "increasingly scientifically based workforce"; and there is also the perceived need for "wise political decision-making" on matters ranging from genetics to the environment. To the Science Establishment, these justify large-scale efforts to include science in all levels of education, from kindergarten through post-graduate education. Presumably, a more scientifically literate populace would come to the right conclusions—and vote accordingly—on social policy issues. Citizens with knowledge of molecular genetics would be better employees of health- and agriculture-related life sciences corporations. Drivers would make better purchasing decisions with knowledge about the relative impacts of Hummers and hybrid cars on global warming. Americans with environmental engineering degrees would be more likely to understand real estate developers when they present storm water run-off plans to a county commission.

The impediments to scientific literacy, as identified by the Science Establishment, include the following:

- Most elementary school teachers lack even a rudimentary education in science and mathematics.

- Teachers of math and science have crushing teaching loads that make it nearly impossible for them to perform well.

- Present science textbooks and methods of instruction, far from helping students, often impede progress toward scientific literacy. They emphasize information instead of understanding; memory at the expense of critical thought; and the rote learning of answers rather than the exploration of questions.

- The present curricula in science and mathematics are overstuffed and undernourished—topics are taught over and over again in needless detail.[7]

Improving scientific literacy, therefore, involves improving teacher education, revising textbooks, and changing instructional methods. These are outlined in the AAAS's Project 2061 handbook (and website[8]), though they have been echoed by most of the Science Establishment's initiatives. Improved teacher training, better educational materials, and re-structured curricula are all eminently practical objectives, and AAAS and NCEF can point with some pride at the successes of implementing their standards and programs under Project 2061.

Even with these "successes," however, there is a philosophical and perhaps ethical issue that needs to be discussed: namely, what are the champions of scientific literacy really *promoting*?

According to the National Academy of Sciences, "scientific literacy is knowledge and understanding of the scientific concepts and processes required for personal decision making, participation in civic and cultural affairs, and economic productivity."[9] I will call this The Broad Definition. According to this view, students and adults who are scientifically literate:

1. Have the knowledge and understanding of scientific concepts and processes required for participation in a Digital Age society.

2. Can ask, find, or determine answers to questions derived from curiosity about everyday experiences.

3. Have the ability to describe, explain, and predict natural phenomena.

4. Are able to read and understand articles about science in the popular press and engage in social conversation about the validity of the conclusions.

5. Can identify scientific issues underlying national and local decisions and express positions that are scientifically and technologically informed.

6. Can evaluate the quality of scientific information on the basis of its source and the methods used to generate it.

7. Have the capacity to pose and evaluate arguments based on evidence and apply conclusions from such arguments appropriately.[10]

I would argue that these seven capabilities do not constitute "scientific literacy." Rather, they indicate someone who is generally well informed, and is capable of employing a certain style of reasoning to govern his/her choices and actions. I am not sure the items on this list are even coherent. Furthermore, understanding scientific concepts and processes may be a good thing, but is it a necessary thing? Even in a Digital Age society, one can function perfectly well without any understanding of scientific concepts and process. Nor, finally, should ordinary citizens be expected to predict natural phenomena—although they should indeed be able to understand that when the National Weather Service issues a hurricane warning for their part of the country, they should take the appropriate measures to board up and/or evacuate.

A more programmatically constructive and coherent account of Scientific Literacy was provided by Rutherford & Ahlgren,[11] who outlined a more extensive set of the skills and knowledge that constitute scientific literacy. Here is an abbreviated list of what I call *The Gory Details*.

Numerical and Computational Skills

Individuals must be able to memorize and instantly recall certain number facts:

- The sums, differences, and products of whole numbers from 1 to 10.
- The decimal equivalents of key common fractions—halves, thirds, two-thirds, fourths, three-fourths, fifths, tenths, and hundredths (but not sixths, sevenths, ninths, or other fractions rarely encountered by most people).
- The relation between decimal fractions and percentages (such as the equivalence of 0.23 and 23 percent).

- The relations among 10, 100, 1,000, 1 million, and 1 billion (for example, knowing that 1 million is a thousand thousands). Expressed as powers of 10, these relations are, successively, 10^1, 10^2, 10^3, 10^6, and 10^9.

- The addition of any two two-digit numbers.

- The multiplication and division of any number by 2, 10, and 100, to one or two significant digits.

Manipulation and Observation Skills

Individuals should be able to do the following:

- Keep a notebook, in which one accurately describes observations and carefully distinguishes actual observations from ideas and speculations about what was observed. The notebook should be understandable weeks or months later.

- Store and retrieve computer information using topical, alphabetical, numerical, and key-word files, and use simple files of one's own devising.

- Enter and retrieve information on a computer, using standard software.

- Use appropriate instruments to make direct measurements of length, volume, weight, time interval, and temperature. Besides selecting the right instrument, this skill entails using a precision relevant to the situation (for example, measuring to the nearest quarter-inch is not good enough for making a cabinet, but is better than what is needed for building a long fence).

- Take readings from standard meter displays, both analog and digital, and make prescribed settings on dials, meters, and switches.

- Make electrical connections with various plugs and sockets and screw terminals, exercising reasonable safety.

- Shape, fasten, and unfasten common materials (such as wood, clay, paper, plastics, and metal) using ordinary hand and power tools, exercising reasonable safety.

- Dilute and mix dry and liquid materials (in the kitchen, garage, or laboratory) in prescribed proportions, exercising reasonable safety.

- Do simple troubleshooting on common mechanical and electrical systems, identifying and eliminating some possible causes of malfunction (in a house, a problem can be the result of a burned-out bulb, an unplugged cord, or a faulty cord or switch; in an automobile, an empty gas tank can cause a problem just like a run-down battery can).

- Compare consumer products on the basis of basic features, performance, durability, and cost, making supportable personal trade-offs.

- Look for the implications of changes in one part of a system—inputs, outputs, or connections—for the operation of other parts.

Communication Skills

- Express orally and in writing the basic ideas covered by the recommendations in this report. This requires, above all, that students acquire some understanding of those ideas, build them into their own conceptual structures, and be able to illustrate them with examples and rational argument.

- Be comfortable and familiar with the standard vocabulary appropriate to the main ideas of science, mathematics, and technology, as used in this report. In many schools, science is taught solely as vocabulary, and this is largely what is tested. This approach is disastrous. What is called for, rather, is a level of understanding of science that results in a useful vocabulary.

- Put correct interpretations on the terms "if..., then ...," "and," "every," "not," "correlates with," and "causes."

- Organize information into simple tables.

- Depict information and relationships by drawing freehand graphs to show trends (steady, accelerated, diminishing-return, and cyclic).

- Read values from pie charts and simple bar and line graphs, false-color maps, and two-way data tables. Be able to note trends and extreme values; be able to recognize how the message in a graph is sensitive to the scale chosen.

- Check the correspondence among tabular, graphic, and verbal descriptions of data.

- Write and follow procedures in the form of step-by-step instructions, recipes, formulas, flow diagrams, and sketches.

- Comprehend and use basic geometrical relationships, including perpendicular, parallel, similar, congruent, tangent, rotation, and symmetry.

- Find and describe locations on maps, using rectangular and polar coordinates.

- Participate in group discussions on scientific topics. To do this, one should be able to restate or summarize what others have said; ask for clarification or elaboration; and take alternative perspectives.

And, finally:

Critical-Response Skills

People should learn to recognize and interrogate weak arguments. They should react skeptically when:

- The premises of the argument are not made explicit.

- The conclusions do not follow logically from the evidence (for example, the statement "Most rich people vote Republican" does not prove the converse, "Most people who vote Republican are rich").

- The argument is based on an analogy, but the comparison is not apt.

- Fact and opinion are intermingled; opinions are presented as facts; or fact and opinion aren't carefully distinguished.

- Celebrity is used as authority. ("Film star endorses new diet.")

- Vague attributions are used in place of specific references (for example, "leading doctors say…"; "science has shown that…"; "compared to some other states…"; and "the scientific community recommends that…").

- No mention is made, in self-reported opinions or information, of measures taken to guard against deliberate or unconscious distortion.

- No mention is made, in evidence said to come from an experiment, of control groups very much like the experimental group.

- Graphs are used that distort the appearance of results. (This is commonly done by chopping off part of the scale; using unusual scale units; or using no scale at all.)

- It is implied that all members of a group—such as "teenagers," "consumers," "immigrants," or "patients"—have nearly identical characteristics that do not overlap those of other groups.

- Average results are reported, but the amount of variation *around the average* is not reported.

- A percentage or fraction is given, but not the total sample size (as in "9 out of 10 dentists recommend…").

- Absolute and proportional quantities are mixed (as in "3,400 more robberies in our city last year, whereas other cities had an increase of less than 1 percent").

- Results are reported with misleading preciseness (for example, 13 out of 19 students is represented as 68.42 percent).

- Explanations or conclusions are represented as the only ones worth considering, with no mention of other possibilities.[12]

Taken as a whole, what Rutherford and Ahlgren proposed doesn't constitute a test of scientific *literacy* so much as scientific *competence*, and the list is even more demanding than (and sometimes quite unlike) what goes on in actual scientific practice. Shamos (1999) noted that achieving broad public competence in these skill-areas is unrealistic at best, and considering them to be constitutive of scientific *literacy* is wrongheaded. Shamos proposed, instead, his own conception of scientific literacy, which involves *understanding*:

- The purpose of science
- The purpose of technology
- Why both science and technology are necessary
- The meaning of scientific "fact"
- The meaning of scientific "truth"
- The role of theory in science
- The role of conceptual schemes in science
- The role of experiment in science
- The role of mathematics in science
- The complementary roles of science and technology
- The history of science—especially technology
- The horizons of science—its potential and limitations

- The societal impact of science and technology
- The proper use of expert science advice
- The roles of statistics in science in decision-making
- The threat of anti-science and science counterculture movements[13]

Shamos' criteria are an improvement on Rutherford and Ahlgren's. While they identified the marks of a person who has been *trained* in "scientific habits of mind,"[14] Shamos captures the sense that "literacy" means being *educated*: "knowing about" science more than "knowing how" to do science. This rings true.

Now suppose that by 2061 we will have managed to teach 95% of the American public either the skills in Rutherford and Ahlgren's lists or the understandings in Shamos'. We will possibly have retained our global technological and economic hegemony, and people will be more knowledgeable; but will America be a better place to live?

Can Scientific Literacy Be Achieved? (And Should It?)

Despite the conventional wisdom behind the Science Establishment's "improved education" model, there are two reasons why *The Broad Definition, The Gory Details*, and even Shamos' concept of scientific *literacy* are problematic. First, all of these are based on the assumption that scientific literacy is required for "personal decision making, participation in civic and cultural affairs, and economic productivity."[15] Second, attempting to inculcate scientific literacy may not be possible (even if desirable), given that many Americans simply have no interest in, or use for, the concepts, skills, or understandings being promoted.

To understand the first assumption, consider the following biographical sketch.

> There is this fellow, call him Ralph, who is a barber. Ralph has been a barber since he completed barber school right after he graduated from high school. Ralph knows how to cut hair well, and makes a decent enough living to support a wife (who is disabled and cannot work outside the home) and two small children. Ralph knows how to cut hair, collect his payment, and make change. He knows how to drive, how to shop, and a myriad of other things. Ralph and his family attend Christian church every Sunday. The children do well in school (with no homework help from Ralph), and they are all happy. Ralph is also active in his community: he attends School Board and City Council meetings, pays attention, and speaks his mind whenever an issue directly affects him or his family. By all rights Ralph is a functioning,

productive member of society, with one exception: Ralph is ignorant, sometimes deliberately so. Ralph listens to every person who sits in his barber chair, all of whom have opinions on all sorts of things, and Ralph internalizes each of these opinions as if he had carefully researched them and independently discovered their truth. It doesn't matter that many of these opinions contradict each other. Ralph takes them in as truth (although he sometimes has heated arguments with his brother-in-law the sociology professor). So far, Ralph is doing quite well in his life, despite being knowledgeable about few scientifically based concepts, unless one counts knowing that putting gas in the car makes it go and paying one's bills guarantees the electricity won't be turned off. He has many skills/abilities and understands much, but lacks much more than he has.

It is presumptuous to suggest that Ralph is illiterate or ignorant, or that his life would be better if he were more scientifically literate. Certainly, someone in Ralph's life has to be scientifically literate: his doctor, his car mechanic, or his handyman/repairman. The point is, one cannot assume that a single set of knowledge-facts are "required for personal decision making, etc." There are a lot of Ralphs in the United States who are living whole, productive lives, and it is wrong to assume that scientific literacy (or even more education and understanding) would improve the quality of their lives. In some ways, it may even diminish it.

Proponents of scientific literacy have a blind spot: values. But the attempt to change people's values under the auspices of making them "literate" raises more important issues.

This is where I turn to the postmodernism referred to in the title of this chapter. Postmodernism has largely been discredited as a *normative* theory in philosophy and the arts,[16] but there are *descriptive* elements in postmodern analysis that are relevant to this discussion. Postmodernism has been defined in many ways, and not always consistently; but one steady theme is that contemporary society is marked by the absence of a single, unifying philosophical foundation on which objective truths can be based. There are no grounding principles that govern values; in other words, no foundation for Truth and Good. François Lyotard, a leading proponent of postmodern thinking, refers to the philosophical foundations we inherited from the Enlightenment—rationalism and empiricism—as "metanarratives." Lyotard argues that metanarratives have lost their power not only to convince, but also to legitimize as "privileged" certain claims to truth and moral rightness. In the transition from modern to postmodern, Lyotard argues, metanarratives have been (and, he believes, should be) replaced by "*petit récits*," "small stories," more modest and "localized" narratives. These small stories, told in groups of varying sizes, are what hold communities and cultures together, and also place them in contrast to, or in conflict with, other communities/cultures.[17]

In a similar vein, Alasdair MacIntyre has argued that our contemporary *moral* culture lacks any unifying theme, prime criterion, or *raison d'être*. What is left of "common morality"—if there is any—is a hollow shell of platitudes and rules that, while helping to maintain a civil society in some regards,[18] fails to give clear moral guidance in the face of new personal, economic, technological, political, or environmental challenges. People cling to slogans; discourse breaks down into shouting matches between those of different value systems. While Lyotard embraces the chaos that results when Truth and Right are supplanted by stories and sentiments, MacIntyre laments the loss.[19]

Lyotard and MacIntyre give us a framework with which to view much of contemporary American society. But James Davidson Hunter[20] went a step further when he identified one result of our postmodern "disintegration"—what has come to be called culture wars. Hunter maintains that the loss of metanarrative has had one striking effect: virtually every issue over which there can be disagreement in modern society has indeed become a "battleground" issue, with no rational solution. While some observers have suggested that the culture wars essentially ended on 9/11/01, consider these continuing "Fields of Battle":

- Abortion
- Adolescent violence
- Cancer treatment
- Capital punishment
- Cloning
- Creation-Evolution, Intelligent Design
- Criminal rehabilitation
- Drug prohibition
- Drug rehabilitation

- Genetic engineering
- Global warming
- Homosexuality
- Immigration
- Race and intelligence
- Right to die, euthanasia
- Sexual education and abstinence only
- Stem cell research

Lyotard, MacIntyre, and Hunter's analyses suggest that none of these issues can be settled through an informed, rational debate. A consensus is unachievable.

The triumph of the Enlightenment, and the advent of Modernism in the West, meant that people substituted *reason* for antiquated *faith*. In matters of

Truth and Right,[21] religious authoritarianism gave way to rational thought, methodical insistence on evidence, and moral principles based on an understanding of human nature. Biblical and Papal authoritarianism was undermined by the search for objective criteria; and *this* became the basis for Truth, not claims based on the Bible. At some time between the 16th and late 20th centuries, undoubtedly with the assistance of positivist, Marxist, and deconstructionist philosophers, and probably with the growth and pervasiveness of mass media—first television and now the Internet—the Enlightenment project was either rejected or simply abandoned. Religious authoritarianism did not once again fill the void (at least in the West). Rather, we are now left with multiple conceptions of what counts as rational, varied and often contradictory methods for grounding claims about truth, and moral systems based on fear, wishful thinking, or blind adherence to a self-appointed leader.[22]

Neither science nor religion now provides an adequate base from which people can collectively understand or resolve problems, and form consensuses. The "answer" to contentious or disputed issues comes down to whatever value-system and belief-set a given individual or group might hold. Science and even organized religion may now themselves be just part of the postmodern condition.

For example, instead of religion, there are religions: In the U.S., we find Evangelical Protestants, Mainline Protestants, Catholics, Eastern (a.k.a. Orthodox) Christians, Mormons, Jews, Muslims, Baha'i, Buddhists, Hindus, Jains, Sikhs, Tao, and Zoroastrians.[23] Although 77% of Americans identified themselves as Christians in 2001, they self-affiliated with 635 different denominations and more than 500,000 individual congregations.[24] A 2001 study warned that within Protestantism (with the largest number of denominations), "there is very considerable diversity…regarding core beliefs," and pointed to an "erosion of the church's foundations."[25] Rather than providing a monolithic unifying social force or a pervasive metanarrative, religion itself appears to be in a postmodern condition, having become just another set of stories competing with the plethora of stories for people's attention and respect.[26]

Thirty-eight percent of Americans believe that Creationism should replace evolution in grade school science classes. However, thousands of Christian clergy have embraced the Clergy Letter Project that endorses Evolution.[27] Twenty-five percent of Americans believe in astrology—not as "entertainment," but as "real."[28] Statistics only begin to show the extent to which "religious" beliefs, as well as other beliefs and attitudes, vary widely across the various cultures of America. It might be argued that these observations lead to the conclusion that contemporary

American society is just pluralistic, much as it always has been. We are a nation of many nationalities, many religious affiliations, many heritages, and as a result we are collectively a "tossed salad"[29] rather than the once-mythologized "melting pot." Or it might be that we are just "multicultural" in the sense that different cultures live and work side-by-side, Turkish-Americans interacting with African-Americans and Paraguayan-Americans. Pluralism and multiculturalism, along with "diversity," may all be characteristic of American (and certainly global) society, but there is something deeper than this in the clash of basic worldviews and guiding values than just the fact that "people are different." Certainly, in the superficial business of living in the U.S., people from different cultures—for the most part—co-exist peacefully. However, when something basic to cultural or ethical belief systems is challenged or threatened—or even when there is a just disagreement—there is no common ground to which "reasonable" people can appeal.

Here is where scientific literacy comes back into play. The notion that increasing scientific literacy will improve our individual lives, and our collective quality of life, by giving people a common ground on which to make judgments about contentious matters, is, in this context, misguided. Some studies purport to show that people's attitudes about a particular issue will change with "more information."[30] Not surprisingly, national science leaders love to cite these studies. And no wonder: they seem to suggest that public attitudes will fall in line with scientists' attitudes if only the public becomes more knowledgeable.

However, it isn't always true that more knowledge leads to more support for science. For example, in the U.S. and around the globe, public attitudes toward genetically modified foods have been shown to grow increasingly negative as more scientific knowledge is provided. This has led to public calls for labeling genetically modified foods, despite the Science Establishment's assurances that genetically modified foods are safe.[31]

It hasn't helped that the Science Establishment has attempted to influence public debates on battleground issues. As a result of its lobbying, science is often (and sometimes correctly) perceived as just another story or belief-system. In what follows, I will argue that the sciences themselves embody different, and sometimes incompatible, belief systems. The idea that scientific literacy will yield consensus on contentious issues—or that the "scientific method" is the only avenue to "The Truth"—is not so apparent, even in the sciences. Not only are the individual sciences different from each other in fundamental ways, but they are themselves scientifically illiterate in many important regards.

Practice and Education in the Sciences: Epistemic Cultures and the Myth of "Science"

In a previously published paper[32], I argued that the sciences have succeeded in training students for science-based roles in our contemporary socio-economic (global) structure. However, I also showed that science students, especially at the college level, are inculcated into a "moral" culture. While they may learn skills, answers, and the way to "produce scientific results," they are also indoctrinated. They learn an ideology. And this ideology holds that non-scientific ways of thinking are non-rational. Moreover, they are taught that values (other than strictly scientific values like carefulness in data collection, honest reporting of results, etc.) generally fall into the realm of the non-scientific, and hence, the non-rational. This belief itself may be a non-scientific belief, and hence non-rational, but that need not worry us at this point.

One assumption I made in my analysis is that all the sciences (including the more mechanistic social sciences, like economics and political science) indoctrinate similarly. That assumption needs to be revisited. Karin Knorr Cetina, in her illuminating book *Epistemic Cultures: How the Sciences Make Knowledge*,[33] shows how two of the sciences, high-energy physics and molecular biology, create knowledge in radically different ways, and indoctrinate practitioners and students alike into two very different sets of beliefs about how one "discovers" facts, what facts there are, who is entitled to claim knowledge of those facts, and, ultimately, what is and is not rational. Knorr Cetina's analysis bolsters the argument that the sciences a) inculcate attitudes of mind and b) exclude consideration of values and beliefs that are contrary to the ones the respective sciences hold dear. Her analysis also suggests that different sciences may even preclude consideration of the "truths" of other fields. In the end, what science really is is a collection of disparate epistemic and moral cultures, none of which can lay claim to "the Truth" except within the boundaries of their own methods, ontological commitments, and worldviews. To expect a non-scientist to understand the nature or purpose of science in this context is to ask the nearly impossible.

Experimental high-energy physics is the science of basic matter and radiation, and how the two interact. In the practice of this science, objects are never directly observed, and knowledge about objects is always mediated or filtered through extremely powerful and complex technological equipment. This field would not exist without computers, superconducting supercolliders, and detectors. Knorr Cetina argues that knowledge obtained from experiments in high-tech laboratories is thus always "unreal." The objects under investigation are "too small ever to be seen except indirectly through detectors, too fast to be captured and contained in a laboratory space, and too dangerous as particle beams to be handled directly."[34] In this context, knowledge is a "representation" of what *appears to be going on,* and scientists are almost obsessively concerned with what Knorr Cetina calls "negative knowledge"—knowledge of the limits of what any given experiment can demonstrate. In high-energy particle physics, "believing is seeing": The scientist "reconstructs" what is occurring in real space-time in a collider-detector in terms of pre-fixed notions of what count as real events, background noise, or distortion of data due to mechanical malfunction. Knowledge in high-energy physics, she concludes, is almost a form of self-congratulation: If nothing in the experiment went wrong, the scientists must have been right in their initial theoretical predictions.

By contrast, molecular biology is a "hands-on" approach to knowing. Observing a microbiology laboratory, one sees workers attending to "small objects present in the laboratory…involved in a pastoral mode of care taking, on the one hand, and…processing programs that transform objects, on the other."[35] Molecular biology, Knorr Cetina argues, is the quintessential "bench" science, in which knowledge is manufactured in small, incremental ways, and where real, living things—from viruses to mice to people—are inextricably linked through a set of physical routines. People use tools to intervene in biological processes, collect and analyze data about those processes, and then return to re-intervene. Knorr Cetina notes that in this science, skilled manual labor—the essential presence of human bodies in knowledge-production—is key.

The kind of knowledge that molecular biology produces, then, while still mediated through various laboratory apparatuses, is hands-on (in its experimental procedures) and "empirical" in the classic sense; ultimately, it is a matter of "seeing is believing." The science is marked by what Knorr Cetina calls "positive knowledge"— knowledge about what we definitely know, which allows the science to progress not via identifying mistakes, but by marking successes. In institutional terms, molecular biology may be a global enterprise, but its real work is performed locally, in individual laoratories. By contrast, high-energy physics demands the global coordination of its practitioners (who perform their jobs in relatively few places). For this and the other reasons, Knorr Cetina concludes that high-energy physics and molecular biology are two distinct "epistemic cultures"—groups of people who do different things, see different things, and believe in different things.

Students of both high-energy physics and molecular biology learn their crafts[36]—controlling machines, performing tasks—in the time-honored tradition of the master-journeyman partnership, all the while assimilating the knowledge-constructs (stories) of the advanced practitioners. There is no need, or time, to ask questions about the point of the experiments, what they contribute to knowledge generally, or how they connect with the experiments going on in other fields. Little thought is given to the implications of making inferences from current experiments or technological interventions in a vacuum, so to speak, devoid of concerns about the historical, social, economic, or ethical dimensions of the work. As students learn the myriad skills and concepts that constitute their disciplines, they learn what and how to believe.[37] An old aphorism about the sciences rings true about both molecular biology and high-energy physics: A bachelor's degree is conferred when one knows something about the field; a master's degree is granted when one can perform the requisite tasks in an experimental setting; and a Ph.D. is bestowed when the practitioner believes in the results of his scientific endeavor. I suspect this applies to most of the individual sciences.

If one were to include in this analysis the study of nanotechnology in materials science—or astronomy, or any of the social sciences—then similar observations would hold. What Knorr Cetina's conclusions imply for this discussion should be clear: As the sciences produce knowledge in their epistemologically distinct ways, they ignore each other, and more importantly, they ignore the history, context, values, implications, etc., of their individual fields as well as their connections (or lack thereof) to other fields. This may be necessary for the individual sciences to manufacture knowledge. It does pose a problem, though, for anyone who would characterize these disparate endeavors as "science" and for anyone who promotes "science literacy."

If scientific fields are so varied and different, then what binds them together as "science?" There are two competing answers. The classic answer is that these disciplines practice and teach something called "the scientific method." But this answer has been almost categorically rejected by philosophers of science. As we have seen, each of the sciences uses concepts, methods, and tools unique to the discipline, in order to generate knowledge unique to that discipline. As numerous studies[38] have shown, there is no single, overarching method. There are only *more or less* systemic sets of practices, tools, and belief-sets.[39] The idea that there is "science" (in contrast with faith or ignorance) is a myth: ". . . it is not one enterprise but many, a whole landscape—or market—of independent epistemic monopolies producing vastly different products."[40]

There's a more accurate socio-historical answer to the riddle of what binds these fields together. The practitioners of all of these crafts refer to their endeavors as sciences, and their collective practices as "science." The senior practitioners of each field have Ph.D.s in their respective disciplines.[41] They believe they have the correct concepts, theories, ontologies, and methodologies to address the questions, objects, and phenomena within their own fields. Moreover, they believe that they alone have the means to explore and explain their intellectual realities. A physicist would not grant the molecular biologist any legitimacy should the biologist make claims about relationships between matter and energy; nor would the biologist grant the physicist the authority to make claims about what the different lines on the chromatograph printout entail for the likelihood that a particular protein has strongly or weakly expressed itself after a DNA transfer.

However, because the practitioners of each of these fields/cultures have been granted advanced degrees by the elders of their respective fields/cultures, their colleagues in other fields often defer to them, honoring their authority. Even if they do not share an epistemological or philosophical metanarrative about what constitutes "the facts," or "scientific truth," they do share a narrative: Members of these groups are entitled to pronounce authoritatively on matters that have "scientific content." They all seem to believe that answers to questions that have scientific dimensions should at the very least be based on "sound science," and that rejecting the scientific answer is non-rational. But this self-conferred legitimacy or authority is precisely what's being challenged, if not ignored, by the larger society. Are scientific truths valid (within the limits of the caveat "pending further study") simply because a scientific community says so? This is germane to the subject of promoting scientific literacy. Why should the public defer to science, even "sound science," on matters such as global warming, abortion, and biotechnology? (Matters, one must note, that are as much about values as science.) Is science literacy good because scientifically literate people will agree with what the scientists say?

The Scientific Literacy Game

There is little doubt that the Science Establishment is a powerful force in contemporary society. The volume of resources, human and financial, that the sciences command is huge. Scientific experts are routinely tapped by the media, by government, and by corporate entities to pronounce, announce, and/or denounce virtually every aspect of our physical, mental, and social lives. There is little doubt, too, that science and technology have changed and improved—and sometimes negatively affected—our world in demonstrable ways. Americans seem to agree, however, that overall, scientists have improved our lives and generally deserve trust and respect.[42] So again, the question: Why the continued push for scientific literacy? Especially when the public appears generally so willing to go along with what the Science Establishment appears to want?

There's an analogy here to a situation that arose in the early 1980s among agricultural leaders and the agricultural research establishment. In the face of growing criticism that agriculture and agricultural science was becoming "out of touch" with American consumers, a study was commissioned by the United States Department of Agriculture (USDA) to examine "agricultural literacy" among both the U.S. public and students of the agricultural sciences. Not surprisingly, the study found that U.S. consumers knew little about modern agriculture, with one exception: some consumers knew that U.S. agriculture "used chemicals" and that some of those chemicals were environmentally dangerous. Most Americans, however, when they thought of farm production, still had images of mom-and-pop "family farms," even if they themselves lived in the Corn Belt or in California's Central Valley. More to the point, the USDA study concluded that students in the agricultural sciences—horticulture, agronomy, soil science, etc.—were themselves also illiterate about farm practices generally. That is, beyond the specific goals and practices of their disciplines (e.g., horticulture students knew how to grow fruits and vegetables, animal science students know about growth rates and nutrition for food animals, etc.), they knew little. The USDA study's conclusion was that the agricultural education system should be retooled so that graduates were "agriculturally literate" and capable of not only educating the non-farm citizenry about farming, but also—and this is key—persuading them *that farming is important.*[43] I refer to this campaign, which aimed to increase public support for agriculture by promoting "agricultural literacy," as the "agricultural literacy game." As a long-time participant in this game, I must confess: *I* think farming is important, and *I* think more people should know about farming. If they did, they would appreciate the fact that Americans pay relatively little for food, and that farmers are among the hardest working people in America. But I also understand that, in making this assertion, I am making a value judgment, and that people who do not care about agriculture are neither ignorant nor simply in need of more "literacy."

Efforts to promote scientific literacy might mean that the Science Establishment is becoming fearful of a decline in scientific capacity or competence—a decline that will affect American competitiveness in science and technology. The Science Establishment may be horrified that so many people believe in Creationism or its intellectual secret agent, Intelligent Design, because this may affect how the rest of the "literate" world perceives the U.S. Science may dread the fact that celebrities promulgate Scientology or Astrology. And—on all these counts—science may well be right.

However, one can see similarities between the current push for scientific literacy and the agricultural literacy game. If people stop believing, or can't be persuaded, that *science is important,* they may be less inclined to support science or endorse science-based policy. They may stop encouraging their children to pursue studies in the various scientific disciplines. Loss of broad public support could mean less funding for superconducting supercolliders, biotechnology research and development, and research on the psychological well-being of laboratory primates. Failure to endorse science-based policy may, down the road, result in demands that genetically modified foods be labeled as such, or that some scientific endeavors (such as cloning food animals, for instance) be halted altogether. Failure to steer children toward mathematics and the sciences might lead to a shortage of the "scientific manpower" that feeds the needs of high-tech corporate giants as well as the classrooms and laboratories that are needed to continue generating more scientific output and more "new and improved" technology.

Over the past 30 years, I have heard calls for greater cultural literacy (from cultural elites in the arts and academia), mathematical literacy (from mathematicians and scientists), historical literacy (from historians and political analysts), and ethical literacy (from theologians, academic philosophers, and the popular media). I would not deny the importance of each of these visions or goals. No one should pretend, however, that they are not also self-serving. Sometimes noble ends can be pursued for self-interested reasons. But the pursuit of noble ends can be robbed of its nobility when the truth about underlying motives is revealed. This is why the call for scientific literacy—as well as the call for supporting the sciences—is essentially a moral or ethical argument. People should be scientifically literate, and agree with scientists when their arguments and conclusions are based on "sound science," because people's lives will be improved, because society will function better, or because God put us on this Earth so we might learn of his creation in ways that have been systematically developed by careful thinkers over the centuries.

It should be clear that the Science Establishment has a vested interest in scientific literacy, even if the kind of knowledge-base and intellectual skills encouraged in Project 2061, in Thamos' offering, and in the various other literacy projects currently underway, are ethically justifiable. Social, economic, political, and even personal considerations suggest that we should continue to promote scientific literacy. However, we should do so with the understanding that we are asking people to value the things we value. If they do not, it is not necessarily because they are irrational, ignorant, or illiterate. Rather, some of them may simply not wish to adopt the goals and values of the individual sciences or the Science Establishment. A modernist believer in Truth and The Good must respect the right of others to believe in Creationism, astrology, Scientology, and the like, even if these are all—scientifically speaking—wrong.

ENDNOTES

1. I.e. efforts such as the AAAS's Project 2061 "Science for All Americans" and the NRC's "National Standards for Science Education" initiative.

2. Around 35% of total degrees awarded between 1966-2004, according to the National Science Foundation's yearly evaluation of degrees granted by U.S. universities.

3. I.e. non-U.S. citizens.

4. National Science Foundation (NSF) Division of Science Resources Statistics, *Science and Engineering Indicators 2006* (Arlington VA: National Science Foundation, 2006).

5. I.V.S. Mullis, M. O. Martin, E. J. Gonzalez, and S. J. Chrostowski, *Findings from IEA's Trends in International Mathematics and Science Study at the Fourth and Eighth Grades* (Chestnut Hill, MA: TIMSS & PIRLS International Study Center, Boston College, 2004);

    National Center for Education Statistics (NCES), "Pursuing Excellence: Comparisons of International Eighth-Grade Mathematics and Science Achievement from a U.S. Perspective, 1995 and 1999" (2000), from http://nces.ed.gov/pubsearch/pubsinfo.asp?pubid=200102 (accessed March 30, 2007).

6. National Academy of Sciences (NAS), *National Science Education Standards*, (Washington, D.C.: National Academy Press, 1996).

7. F. James Rutherford and Andrew Ahlgren, *Science for All Americans* (New York: Oxford University Press, 1991).

8. http://www.project2061.org/.

9. *NAS, 1996.*

10. Ibid.

11. Rutherford and Ahlgren, *Science for All Americans.*

12. Ibid., 175-183.

13. *Morris H. Shamos, The Myth of Scientific Literacy (New Brunswick: Rutgers University Press, 1995).*

14. See John Dewey, *Logic: The Theory of Inquiry* (New York: Holt, 1938).

15. *NAS, 1996.*

16. See Roy D'Andrade, "Moral Models in Anthropology," *Current Anthropology*, 36 (1995): 399-407.

17. Francois Lyotard, *The Postmodern Condition: A Report on Knowledge* (Manchester: Manchester University Press, 1984).

18. I.e. when codified into laws.

19. Alasdair MacIntyre, *After Virtue* (South Bend, IN: University of Notre Dame Press, 1981).

20. James Davidson Hunter, *Culture Wars: The Struggle to Define America* (New York: Basic Books, 1991).

21. John R. Searle, "Rationality and Realism, What Is at Stake?" *Daedalus: Journal of the American Academy of Arts and Sciences* (Fall, 1993).

22. Richard Jensen, "The Culture Wars, 1965-1995: A Historian's Map," *Journal of Social History* 29 (1995): 17-37.

23. Clifford Grammich, *Many Faiths of Many Regions: Continuities and Changes Among Religious Adherents Across U.S. Counties,* RAND Labor and Population working paper series, WR-211 (Santa Monica, CA: Rand Corporation, 2004).

24. Barry A. Kosmin and Ariela Keysar, *Religion in a Free Market: Religious and Non-Religious Americans, Who, What, Why, Where* (Ithaca, NY: Paramount Market Publishing, Inc., 2006).

25. Uwe Siemon-Netto, "Poll Shows Protestant Collapse," http://www.adherents.com/misc/BarnaPoll.html, March 23, 2007.

26. Jonathan Zimmerman, *Whose America? Culture Wars in the Public Schools* (Cambridge: Harvard University Press, 2002).

27. Clergy Letter Project (CLP), 2004.

28. NSF, 2006.

29. Gerald MacCullum, *Political Philosophy* (Upper Saddle River, NJ: Prentice-Hall, 1984).

30. Nick Alexander, *IFIC Survey: Food Biotechnology Not a Top-of-Mind Concern for American Consumers* (Washington, DC: IFIC: International Food Information Council Background Paper, 2005).

31. Priest, 2005.

32. Jeffrey Burkhardt, "Scientific Values and Moral Education in the Teaching of Science." *Perspectives on Science* vol.7, no.1 (December 1999).

33. Karin Knorr Cetina, *Epistemic Cultures: How the Sciences Make Knowledge* (Cambridge: Harvard University Press, 1999).

34. Ibid., 48.

35. Ibid., 81.

36. I.e. they learn "the science."

37. W. W. Cobern, "Science Education as an Exercise in Foreign Affairs," *Science & Education.* 4 (3) (1995): 287-302.

38. Including Knorr Cetina's.

39. See Paul Feyerabend, *Against Method* (London: Verso Press, 1975); Knorr Cetina, 1984.

40. Knorr Cetina, 1999.

41. Jerome Ravetz, *Scientific Knowledge and its Social Problems* (New York: Oxford University Press, 1971).

42. See NSF, 2006.

43. G.K. Douglass, *Cultivating Agricultural Literacy: Challenge for the Liberal Arts* (Battle Creek, MI: W.K. Kellogg Foundation, 1984).

ADDITIONAL SOURCES

Bernstein, Richard. *Dictatorship of Virtue: Multiculturalism and the Battle for America's Future.* New York: Alfred A. Knopf, 1994.

Penn Free Methodist Church. *http://www.realchristianity.org/.* Accessed May 10, 2007.

Priest, S. H. "US Public Opinion Divided Over Biotechnology?" *Nature Biotechnology* 18 (2000): 939-942.

10. The Salience of Secular Values and Scientific Literacy for American Democracy

Barry A. Kosmin & Juhem Navarro-Rivera

The Congruence of Science and Secularism

Embedded in modernity is the idea that science is a major building block of the secular worldview, and that the progress of science is, *de facto*, the triumph of the secular worldview. This outlook arises from the close historical, philosophical, and intellectual relationship between the natural sciences and secular ideas and values. Both secular and scientific values were entrenched within the Enlightenment project of emancipating humanity and actualizing the highest human potentials through the diffusion of knowledge. These goals, in turn, became linked to the quest for liberty, freedom of thought, and popular sovereignty—and thus democracy. The triadic relationship of secular values, scientific literacy, and social and economic progress, and their role as the building blocks of democracy in the United States, is the subject of this chapter. Our purpose is to demonstrate that particularly in the 21st century, in order to achieve a prosperous society and a healthy, participatory democratic order based on secular values, a high degree of science literacy among the citizenry is necessary.

There are indeed many points of congruence between the scientific and the secular, including commitments to reason, skepticism, systematic knowledge, empiricism, and the procedural aspects of scientific methodology—all of which form the basis of a common commitment to the impartial generation of truth. The methodical use of empirical data in scientific research accords with the "worldly" focus of secular ideas and values. Modern science is thus properly considered an agent of secularization because of its association with free inquiry and freedom of thought and expression. It also qualifies by virtue of its role in undermining the superstition, ignorance, and belief in magic that so often fostered fear and authoritarianism in human societies.

The Scientific Revolution of the 17th century involved an unprecedented endeavor to secure the autonomy of the scientific enterprise from religious authority. It established core methodologies that investigators use when they experiment, when they confirm what others have done, when they follow through on the processes of not only generating but testing, confirming, and denying knowledge of one sort or another. This cultivation of a naturalistic worldview and a skeptical spirit encouraged believers and non-believers alike to cultivate a new mental habit of demanding good, empirically verifiable reasons for their beliefs, and to reexamine the factual basis of moral causes. These pioneers envisioned science as a powerful force for social progress.

It was the proponents of Copernicus' theory of a heliocentric universe who began using the phrase *libertas philosophandi* (freedom of philosophizing—free inquiry). This term eventually found its way into the full title of Spinoza's famous *Theological-Political Treatise* of 1670. Galileo proclaimed the fundamental scientific principle that "Two truths cannot contradict each other." In 1660, when the famous Royal Society of London was founded, its members asserted that science was based on the principle of testing ideas by experiment, adopting as their motto "*Nullius in verba*," which, loosely translated, means, "Take nobody's word for granted." They also went on to commit themselves to exclude matters of religion and politics from scientific discussions. In a similar vein in *The Federalist No. 10*, U.S. founding father James Madison[1] warned of the danger passions and factions posed to freedom. By "passions," he meant impulses such as irrationality and demagogy, and by "factions" he meant special interests. Since suppressing and controlling the creation of groups (i.e., regulating the right of association) was against freedom, the best check was a democratic impulse that encouraged voluntary and civic organizations in the Enlightenment-based hope that reason would prevail and extreme and fringe groups would remain just that: marginal, on the fringe. The vehicle for achieving this experiment was the theologically neutral secular state.

The sciences, in terms of their ethos and organization, can also be viewed as the best example of the triumph of the essentially secular ideas embodied in the French Revolution's slogan of *liberté, égalité, fraternité*, and its promise of *la carrière ouverte aux talents*—meritocracy. With its universality, objectivity, and commitment to meritocratic peer review, science seems to admit of egalitarianism and real democracy more than any other area of human enterprise. Its ethos leads to a universalism of good ideas and empirical data that are accepted from whatever quarter they emerge.

Science involves an anti-authoritarian tradition since it is based on the concept of self-generated human progress—constantly reforming and refining itself from within, without external guidance. In the words of the sociologist Max Weber,[2] science is a secular "vocation" and "scientific work is chained to the course of progress…; every scientific 'fulfillment' raises new 'questions'; it *asks* to be 'surpassed' and outdated." In the 20th century, modernist authoritarian movements such as fascism and communism lauded science and invested heavily in it. However, these regimes were ambivalent in their embrace of science, for they still expected science and scientists to be subservient to, and even to buttress, the ruling political ideologies. This led to state-endorsed pseudo-science such as "race theory" and eugenics in Nazi Germany,[3] and Lysenkoism in the Soviet Union.[4]

Today, scientific education and research are commonly viewed as pillars of secular lifestyles and social organizations that, as a matter of principle, reject the authority of any particular religious association or ideological doctrine. Along the lines of Isaiah Berlin's[5] celebrated distinction between "negative" and "positive" conceptions of liberty, science and secularism can thus be seen as congruent because of their common endeavor to demarcate areas of human action that are "free from" external, particularly religious, authority.

Science Education

The interplay of science education and secular values has long been recognized as having public policy importance in a number of areas—particularly with respect to economic prosperity and geopolitical strength. The pivotal role that education plays in fostering labor productivity and, by implication, economic growth—not just as an input linking aggregate output to the stock of productive inputs but also as a factor strongly associated the rate of technological progress—was acknowledged from the time of the Industrial Revolution. In the United States, the dream of harnessing scientific progress to the betterment of all citizens arose during the Progressive era in the early 20th century—the heyday of belief in the public school and the birthplace of the research university. The Progressive idea of universal education and progress, exemplified in the writings of John Dewey, and earlier by Horace Mann, was predicated on the notion that the form of education that can truly empower individuals is scientific in spirit and principle. This idea was originally propagated by a coalition of industrialists, public servants, and academicians who believed that science and its universal method of knowledge acquisition could unify the nation and generate economic and social progress.

This vision assumed that science was and should be value-neutral and indifferent to the varied identities and beliefs of an increasingly diverse American nation. The Progressives professed that the "indifference" of science—its disinterested search for truth—was basic to its credibility and strength.[6] Yet in our time this ideology, which conceives of science as a common good embodying value-neutral knowledge, has come to be disputed by certain communities that feel threatened by the implications of scientific research for their own worldviews. In the academy, a fashionable relativist and postcolonial outlook belittles the achievements of science and instead valorizes "local knowledge" grounded in indigenous or ancient conceptual categories. More importantly, science has come under challenge from a resurgent religious fundamentalism, which above all seeks to protect young people from being taught scientific ideas that seem to threaten religious beliefs.

Paradoxically, the very triumph of science has enhanced its vulnerability to these forms of "skepticism." As it has advanced and grown, science has become more complex and less easy for ordinary people to comprehend. In an age when technology is increasingly user-friendly, it is easy to be indifferent, alienated, or hostile to the scientific enterprise while indulging in the benefits of science-based high-tech industry. Burkhardt[7] has alluded to the widening gap between the scientific community and much of the general public. This intellectual and social divide has gradually eroded the status of science as a common good. Even though most Americans still claim to value science highly and believe it will continue to make their lives better, too many steer clear of it in school. As a result, the traditional model of science education now appears to have become less functional. Although parents recognize that their children's future depends on a good education, the swell of scientific illiteracy prevents them from assessing with confidence and clarity what actually constitutes a good education.

U.S. Educational Performance in Science

It is not too much to say that in the contemporary U.S., the dream of science education for all has become an empty cliché rather than a source of personal inspiration. The result is a mood of ambivalence and confusion among many American science educators. One cause of the negative trend outlined above can be seen in the most recent international comparisons of performance in science among 15-year-old students. The Program for International Student Assessment (PISA) [8] run by the Organization for Economic Co-operation and Development (OECD), a 30-member-nation body, reported that the U.S. rated below average in science and mathematics. On student performance the U.S. mean score is 489 (Finland is top with 563), which is significantly lower statistically than 20 other countries, including its main European and Asian economic competitors such as Canada, Japan, Korea, U.K., Germany, and Hong Kong. PISA felt it necessary to comment that "Countries below the trend line, such as the United States, show lower performance than would be predicted from their GDP per capita." This is not a matter of under-investment in education. Quite the reverse: "Spending per student in Czech Republic and New Zealand are 41% and 57%, respectively, of the spending levels of the U.S. but both are among top performers in PISA." Moreover, American students show as much general interest in science, enjoyment of science, and motivation to learn as in other countries. We have to ask whether there is a cultural or pedagogic problem in science education.[9]

Another statistic from PISA suggests American education has problems of a class nature that require a response from policy makers. PISA performance patterns vary widely across countries. For example, Korea is among the best-performing countries in science in PISA 2007, in terms of students' performance, while the United States performs below the OECD average. Nevertheless, the United States has a similar percentage of students at the top at Levels 5 and 6 (9.1%) as Korea (10.3%). The discrepancy in mean scores between the two countries is partly accounted for by the fact that at the lower levels of proficiency (that is, below Level 2) the United States has 24.4% of students, while Korea has only 11.2%. Across all participating countries students' general appreciation of science is positively associated with their socio-economic background. PISA reports that "This relationship is most pronounced in Ireland and the United States." U.S. official data is confirmatory; the National Assessment of Educational Progress report on urban school districts showed that urban schools where minorities are concentrated lagged badly behind on scientific literacy.[10] These findings validate the statement made earlier concerning a divide between a scientific elite and the general public. In the contemporary U.S. there is a social gap that equates to a knowledge gap in science literacy. When a well-educated, prosperous liberal elite is estranged from the bulk of the population, it is a serious political and public policy issue.

The science literacy gap has wider societal ramifications. The participation rate in elections produces a metric that mirrors that for performance in science education. In 2006, the proportion of voters in the Congressional elections comprised 54% of the adult population.[11] This is a low rate of participation by international standards, but the rate varied immensely by level of education. Only 31% of U.S. citizens with less than a high school education exercised their democratic franchise compared to 72% of those holding at least a college degree. One can conclude that the knowledge gap leads to low self-esteem, alienation, and a general disconnect from civic engagement. That this deficit correlates highly with racial and ethnic minority status is also socially significant. Thus the social gap produces and perpetuates an educational divide and produces a democratic deficit of serious dimensions. That Burkhardt's "Ralph the barber"[12] can remain happily ignorant of science is not just a failure of the Enlightenment project. Such ignorance can be expected to lead him to ignore and evade his responsibilities and duties as a citizen of a democratic republic.

Moreover, Ralph's children cannot long remain ignorant and still hope to maintain their present standard of living and quality of life. The requirements of the United States job markets have evolved over past generations. Recent analysis shows that the steepest decline in task input over the last decade has not been with manual tasks, as is often reported, but with routine cognitive tasks, i.e., those mental tasks that are well described by deductive or inductive rules, and that dominate many of today's middle-class jobs.[13] This suggests that if large numbers of American students learn merely to memorize and reproduce scientific knowledge and skills, they risk being prepared mainly for jobs that are disappearing from labor markets in most advanced industrialized countries.

Economic Performance

There is a cogent economic argument for securing strong baseline science competencies. For most of the 20th century, school science curricula, especially in the later stages of secondary education, tended to focus on providing the foundations for the professional training of a small number of scientists and engineers.[5] This continues to be the U.S. pattern for the top 10% of students. The curriculum mostly presented science in a form that focused on the knowledge of the science disciplines, while paying less attention to knowledge about science and applications relating to citizens' life and living. However, the influence of scientific and technological advances on today's economies, the central place of information technology in employment, and the increasing presence of science and technology-related issues require that all citizens, not just future scientists and engineers, have strong science competencies. The proportion of students at very low proficiency is therefore also an important indicator in terms of citizens' ability to participate fully in society, particularly as voters[15] and in the labor market. PISA and similar authorities have established five levels of science proficiency. Level 2 is regarded as the baseline, defining the level of achievement on the PISA science scale at which students begin to demonstrate the science competencies that will enable them to participate actively in real life situations related to science and technology. One-fourth of American students do not reach this level of proficiency. OECD reports that these students "often confuse key features of an investigation, apply incorrect scientific information, and mix personal beliefs with scientific facts in support of a decision."

The mismatch between the needs of the labor market (on one hand) and the educational skills of young people educated in the American educational system (on the other) is further evident from the following statistics. The proportion of science and engineering occupations in the United States that are filled by postgraduate-educated workers born abroad increased from 14% to 22% between 1990 and 2000, and from 24% to 38% when considering solely doctorate-level science and engineering workers.[16] Irrespective of arguments about the value of immigration to the nation, the reality of the labor markets is that such high-status, well-paid jobs are just not accessible to most young people educated in the U.S. and particularly not to women and U.S.-born minorities, who are particularly under-qualified in science.[17] Thus students graduating from today's American high schools are disadvantaged by their lack of educational preparation for careers in science and engineering.

Voters and Electoral Politics

There is also a non-economic argument for raising the level of science literacy for the mass of Americans whose level of science education does not place them in the elite 10%. As we shall demonstrate, the average voter is now asked about (and will increasingly be required to deliberate on) ballot questions and "political" arguments that involve a high level of scientific literacy: questions and issues such as nuclear energy, radiation, genetically modified (GM) crops, acid rain, greenhouse effects, as well as health and personal well-being issues: sunscreens, exercise, nutrition, and vaccination.

Given the frequency and civic importance of American elections, having an educated voting public is a matter of necessity in the United States. Americans go to the polls every year to decide a myriad of public offices for municipal, county, state, and federal governments—offices ranging from local commissioner of sanitation to the President. Moreover, Americans not only elect representatives and public officers but vote simultaneously in referenda and ballot initiatives. While most of the decisions can be (and in many ways are) made using ideological shortcuts such as political party partisanship, in the increasingly complex scientific and technological climate in which we live these days scientific developments require a nonpartisan decision-making approach.

In recent elections stem cell funding initiatives made it onto the ballots of two states: California (2004) and New Jersey (2007). In Missouri, in 2006, a similar quest led to a constitutional amendment ballot. Thus the general public cannot escape from engagement with science issues on the societal and personal levels. In fact, in an age of bio-medical advances, energy shortages and environmental crises due to climate change, the public and the voters will be increasingly called upon to evaluate scientific data and arguments. Of course, the lawyers, judges, and the courts will be even more closely involved. A signal example was the New Jersey 2007 ballot about floating a $450 million bond issue for a taxpayer-funded stem cell research program. As one might have predicted, even before the voters got a chance to decide, conservative groups tried unsuccessfully in the courts to derail the vote because they claimed the advisory statement accompanying the ballot was misleading on scientific grounds.[18] Of course, the advisory statement is what the voting public has to read if it wants to properly evaluate the proposal.

The partisan alignment in these state votes—especially in Missouri—is remarkable. In the case of Missouri's stem cell amendment, the election was extremely close (51-49%) in favor of the amendment. It was an election primarily decided by Missouri's independent voters. Republicans rejected the amendment by a margin of 76-24%, while Democrats voted in favor by the exact same margin.[19] Here we have a politically neutral decision, a vote on science policy, that became political fodder for party elites and groups at the extremes of the political debate.

A similar situation occurred in California in 2004, and again in 2006, though the voting was not as polarized, perhaps because the science and tax issues were somewhat muddled up. In 2004 a stem cell funding initiative was passed 59-41%. In this case the differences between Democrats and Republicans were not as marked; 64% of Republicans rejected the proposal while 80% of Democrats supported the measure. The California independents voted for the proposal 60-40%.[20] In a 2004 initiative regarding funding alternative fuels, California voters rejected the proposal 55-45%. The partisan splits were Democrats 65% in favor of the proposal, Republicans 71% against the proposal, and independents 52% against the proposal.[21]

These votes represent several problems regarding scientific literacy. First, they show extreme partisan splits in which Democrats overwhelmingly support ballot initiatives related to science policy and Republicans overwhelmingly reject them. Stuck in the middle are independents, who have both supported and rejected policies. These voting splits highlight a feature of recent politics whereby the Republicans emerge as an anti-science constituency. Much of this trend has to do with the conservative Christian constituency that is now part of the core of the Republican Party[22] and the linkage of religious conservatism to anti-scientific ideas.[23] This has alienated the Republican Party from the mainstream scientific discourse and led it to promote pseudo-sciences such as Intelligent Design Creationism,[24] global warming denialism, and the rejection of programs on embryonic stem cell research under pro-life activist pressure.[25]

Figure 10-1
State Ballot Initiatives and Referenda by Decade, 1904-2006

Period	Total	Average per election
1900-1909	23	7.7
1910-1919	274	27.4
1920-1929	189	21.0
1930-1939	257	28.6
1940-1949	159	19.9
1950-1959	127	18.1
1960-1969	98	14.0
1970-1979	177	17.7
1980-1989	247	24.7
1990-1999	379	37.9
2000-2006	301	43.0
Source: Initiative and Referendum Institute		

At the same time, we must hold the Democratic Party accountable as well. If Democratic voters are making science policy decisions based solely on partisanship, without regard for costs and feasibility, they are not really helping the cause of science. They are surrendering their rationality to party loyalty, even if it's a party that actually supports the science establishment nearly all the time. This is because, contrary to Burkhardt's opinion[26] the goal of science education is not to have the public "rubber stamp" the decisions scientists favor, but to have a rational public that understands, at a basic level, the costs and benefits of implementing such policies.

Another key fact is that whether we like it or not, ever more complicated decisions are falling into the hands of voters. The Initiative and Referendum Institute (IRI) at the University of Southern California, which tracks data on citizen initiatives, has found that since the 1990s, the voters have been deciding an increasing number of policies at the state level.[27] *Figure 10-1* shows the number of initiatives by decade, starting in 1904—when progressives started to gain ground in getting their reforms adopted—and ending in 2006.

The left-hand column shows the decade while the center column shows the total number of initiatives proposed in that decade. The right-hand column

Figure 10-2
Self-Reported Voter Turnout by Education Level, 2004, 2006

	2006		2004	
Education	United States	Missouri	United States	California
High School or Less	42%	48%	59%	57%
Some College	56%	62%	77%	74%
College Graduate	69%	75%	86%	82%
Post Graduate Degree	78%	88%	92%	89%
Total	54%	60%	72%	71%
Source: Current Population Survey, Data FERRETT				

represents the average number of proposals by year (only counting years within that decade that featured referenda or initiatives). During the heyday of the Progressive Era in the 1920s and 1930s, the average number of referenda peaked at 28.56/year during the period from 1930-1939. It never again rose over 20 initiatives per year until the period of 1980-1989. The 1990s represented the highest (raw) number of initiatives being presented to voters, and the current uncompleted decade is on pace to surpass the 1990s figure, already topping 300 and an average of 43 per election.

The IRI does not have a category of science policy questions in its database, although, browsing through the tables, it is clear that citizens have been asked about issues such as abortion, several policies concerning the environment and energy, and, of course, the biotech-related stem cell questions. Knowing more about science might help this decision-making process. It is irresponsible to think that because science is complicated, or scientific knowledge is not critical to the average person's daily survival, he or she can ignore the deepening educational void among the voting public. The anti-democratic alternative would be to remove the decision-making process from the people and leave it to technocrats (or elites). Regrettably, this is what is indirectly occurring since, as mentioned above, there is a real gap in participation in which the less-educated refrain from participating in elections and referenda in higher proportions than those with better education, as *Figure 10-2* clearly demonstrates. On average, around half of the least educated stay away from the polls while most of the most highly educated vote.

Figure 10-3 shows that the actual pattern of voting is less linear or polarized than turnout. However, there is a tendency for the best educated voters in

Figure 10-3
Vote by Education Level on Stem Cell Research Initiatives in California and Missouri[28]

Education	Missouri, 2006		California, 2004	
	Yes	No	Yes	No
High School or Less	53%	47%	55%	45%
Some College	48%	52%	60%	40%
College Graduate	50%	50%	59%	41%
Post Graduate Degree	57%	43%	65%	35%
Source: CNN				

California, the most populous state in the U.S., to be most supportive of science.

Polarization and extremism, even when one of those extremes tends to "agree" with the scientific mainstream or consensus, should not be the basis of policy decisions regarding science. Instead, we need an educated, rational public that can discern and critically determine which science policies to follow and which ones to dismiss. Considering that the recent explosion of citizen initiatives came after the end of the Cold War, this process seems to be one of "devolution" or returning to the people the power that was exercised during the Cold War by Eisenhower's famous "Military-Industrial Complex." Of course, this powerful "complex" was (and remains) very much a science and technology-based interest group, so in the interests of prudence and the common good it requires careful monitoring.

Elected Officials and Public Servants

We have focused so far on the need for the electorate to become more scientifically literate. However, we must also hold our elected leaders accountable. Polarization has not only occurred among voters. It might actually be more pronounced among elites. Several studies[29] have found that, ideologically speaking, party leaders and elected officials have moved to the extremes. Though we can track the beginning of this elite polarization to the 1970s,[30] this polarization has been exacerbated in recent decades.[31]

One reason ideology may have displaced reasoned discussion in this sphere is that there is a dearth of scientists and engineers elected to Congress. Whereas one-third of the members of the House in the 108th Congress were lawyers (JDs), only 18 members (or less than 1%) had a Ph.D.[32] And even then, not all the doctorates were in science. Given the increasing need for scientific regulation in the fields of telecommunications, public health, and biotechnology, for example, there is an obvious need for a body that can assist the current batch of elected officials in making sound judgments based on scientific evidence. Unfortunately, such a body once existed but is no more. The Office of Technology Assessment (OTA), a body that provided Congress with independent scientific analysis, was dismantled following the "Republican Revolution" of 1994.[33] In the case of the OTA, ideology (i.e., hostility to government, bureaucracy, and regulation) trumped reason and the common good.

Recommendations

Improvements in scientific literacy and science education appear critical to the future of democracy and the economy in the United States. One of the reasons is because "we the people" are being asked more often to make policy decisions that are intellectually beyond "our" reach and understanding. It can be argued that a scientifically illiterate electorate, today more than at any other juncture in American history, is seriously detrimental to the future survival of the nation. Yet, as has been shown, questions are being voted on by a largely uninformed and polarized electorate. In addition, a large segment of less educated Americans now exclude themselves from involvement in the democratic process.

One strategy for resolving this democratic deficit is to improve science education. The science establishment's new Committee on Prospering in the Global Economy of the 21st Century[34] proposes a project for "10,000 teachers, One Million minds." This is an initiative to get the brightest students interested in spreading science. The Committee also proposes "K-12 Curricular Materials Based on World-Class Standards." There are other recommendations in the same vein of strengthening science education, e.g., providing students with more laboratory experience,[35] and incentives for college and graduate education. Alas, these ideas somehow fail to address the issue of promoting "critical thinking" among students and focus on a rather narrow definition of what is educationally important.

Without getting into the specific institutional barriers—such as federalism— which militate against a standardized national science education curriculum in American schools, the problem is that this solution only addresses the needs of school-age children. In the meantime, and probably into the future, we need to make up for past deficiencies with remedial solutions that address the general public. In theory, the burgeoning media and new communication technologies offer an ideal vehicle for "remedial adult or informal education" in science. In reality, this probably requires massive public funding, which is very unlikely to be provided.

Another possibility is to increase citizen participation.[36] The problem is: what constitutes citizen participation? If it means merely throwing out questions for debate, we are failing. As the California and Missouri voting statistics by party identification clearly showed, even the half of the adult population that bothers to vote makes decisions based on party loyalties without necessarily thinking about them objectively. One possibility is a return to the ideals and practices of the past with attempts to revive the civic-minded and engaged society described by Alexis de Tocqueville in *Democracy in America*.[37] De Tocqueville was amazed at the levels of associational life existing in America in the 1830s and how they helped to promote democracy and progress—even at a time when franchise was limited to white men. Fast-forward about 200 years and we are faced with a decline of civic involvement in America.[38] This decline in civic involvement and real debate can be linked to the polarization of political discourse because those who are presently actively participating are those who tend to have more extreme opinions, and as such are less likely to compromise on most issues.[39]

Successful examples of methods to heighten public awareness of science-based public policy issues come from the United Kingdom, where a large section of the general public was educated about issues such as GM crops and the environment through focus groups and town meetings.[40] Of course, in the present U.S. political climate this type of activity would be labeled "advocacy" by opponents. This "informal public education" model has been adopted by former Vice-President and recent Nobel Prize laureate Al Gore, with his movie *An Inconvenient Truth,* his lecture tour and campaign to raise awareness about global warming, and his books such as *The Assault on Reason*.[41] Nevertheless, this approach can only reach a finite amount of people and seems to target college students and other well-educated members of the public. To become more widespread, it needs greater local mobilization. In this way it might improve the sense of efficacy among the public, especially among those who so far have been left out of the discussion and the political process altogether.

Another communication idea comes from Nisbet and Mooney[42] and their "Framing Science" approach, in which they exhort scientists to "learn to actively 'frame' information to make it relevant to different audiences." Unfortunately, most of their article focuses on pandering to religious fundamentalists instead of really educating a less passionate and more disengaged core of the population.

Advocacy on behalf of rationalism and science has recently become more common. The Center for Inquiry, the publisher of the magazines *Free Inquiry* and *Skeptical Inquirer,* has recently expanded its operations on behalf of rationalism and in 2007 launched itself as a public policy lobbying group for science in Washington, D.C. In a similar fashion, a group of scientists and other interested parties have been pushing for a 2008 presidential science debate,[43] and a website (www.sciencedebate2008.com) has been created for that purpose.

Obviously, there is a growing concern about the need to address scientific (il)literacy among our elected officials. The country requires more politicians with a willingness and ability to engage with science-related issues, and with the ideas of science. One way to do this is to change the educational profile of elected officials and so reduce the number of lawyer-politicians. This requires more scientists to become active in public life and public debate and so provide greater critical analysis of scientific policies. We are seeing some signs of this tendency with the emergence of high-profile scientist-bloggers such as Greg Laden, PZ Myers, and Phil Plait, all of whom provide some political commentary in their blogs. A key immediate public policy need is the restoration by Congress of the Office of Technology Assessment. In fact, a restoration of OTA would be a great leap forward in alleviating the lack of scientific literacy among the members of Congress, and bloggers such as Mooney[44] and Myers[45] have promoted this idea in their blogs.

So what should be our intellectual and educational goals for the properly qualified, scientifically literate, 21st-century American voter and politician? Obviously the geometric growth in scientific knowledge and its increasing disciplinary differentiation poses a knowledge problem. Not even the most eminent scientist can keep up with the massive output of scientific knowledge in the contemporary world. What is feasibly required is a "meta-science" approach to science education, focusing on an immersion in scientific method and critical thinking. One aspiration should obviously be the ability to distinguish between evidence-based explanations and personal opinions about science-related issues. Another is an awareness of how science and technology shape our material, intellectual, and cultural environments. For example, Americans need an ability to recognize and explain the role of technologies as they influence the nation's economy, social organization, and culture. This means that despite all the difficulties involved over the long haul, science education in U.S. schools needs to be recalibrated so that it both improves quality and assists equality of outcomes. The democratic imperative of American society requires a participatory citizenry that is confident in its ability to evaluate both its own best interests and the common good. To this end the scientific literacy that the "aware citizen" needs is an understanding that in science there are no absolute truths, no sacred cows, and no final secrets to be discovered that will allow all scientists in a field to retire and go home. Instead, our ideal citizen should know that all hypotheses and theories are subject to modification and even replacement as new research and discoveries become available. So students should emerge from school knowing that science is not dogmatic, and those who try to present it dogmatically are doing it a disservice. For as Millar says: "if one major purpose of science education is to equip students to respond to socio-scientific issues, this requires an understanding of the nature of scientific knowledge."[46]

One would also hope that the model American citizens of the future will be able to understand the definitions of commonly used terms. Perhaps most importantly they need to understand what "burden of proof" means. They are likely to meet this term in their civic role as a juror as it refers to legal matters, but they also need to know how it applies in other fields of human endeavor, like philosophy and science. Here we must remember that the average American is asked as a juror to make judgments in legal cases about DNA evidence and other scientific matters that are left to professional magistrates and judges in the law courts of most of Europe. Thus the average citizen needs to know that every affirmative statement carries a "burden of proof." Yet this burden does not imply proving something beyond a shadow of a doubt, but rather the responsibility to provide logical reasons for one's position. If one makes a public statement, then one has the burden of providing evidence for that statement. Furthermore, given the ever-more-demanding role of juror and voter, there may even be an argument for teaching basic philosophy and logic in 21st-century American high schools (as they do in France). That way, the populace would be able to recognize, for instance, that being skeptical is not the same as making affirmative statements that things are or are not. Americans would know that the essence of the skeptic is to question, not just to deny things.

The contemporary world situation—in which knowledge, particularly in scientific and technological fields, equals power—makes increasing intellectual demands on what many regard as a "dumbed-down" society. Unfortunately, the logic of history still seems to involve fierce global competition such that the average 21st-century American will not be able to flourish or perhaps even survive as a worker, juror, voter, or even consumer without a higher degree of science literacy. Those who are concerned with the future welfare of the nation should insist upon a higher degree of knowledge relevant to a technologically advanced civilization. This means getting more scientists out of the laboratory and into the world. There is a need for more men and women educated in science getting involved in journalism and communications, government and political parties, and grassroots organizations. Or as Mooney says: "we need more scientists with additional skills to boot." [47]

In the contemporary globalized world there is a premium on the integration of concepts and ideas. Science and technology can no longer be seen as isolated practices, but rather as activities that underpin every aspect of social and economic policy, and hence all aspects of government. This is known as "joined up" thinking. We would argue that we should extend this "thinking" to the nature of the linkage among secular values, science literacy and democracy. A major challenge for the 21st century is to raise the awareness of the American public and its leaders to this linkage.

ENDNOTES

1. A. Hamilton, J. Madison, and J. Jay, *The Federalist papers* (New York: Signet Classic, 1999), C. Rossiter, ed.

2. M. Weber, "Science as a Vocation" (2004), from http://www.molsci.org/research/publications_pdf/Max_Weber,_Science_a15767A.pdf (accessed on December 20, 2007).

3. M. Burleigh, *The Racial State: Germany 1933-1945* (Cambridge University Press, 1991).

4. N. Krementsov, *Stalinist Science* (Princeton University Press, 1997); V.N. Soyfer, *Lysenko and the Tragedy of Soviet Science* (New Brunswick, NJ: Rutgers University Press, 1994).

5. I. Berlin, "Two Concepts of Liberty," in R. E. Goodin and P. Pettit, eds., *Contemporary Political Philosophy: An Anthology* (Blackwell Publishing, 1997), 648.

6. K. F. Zuga, "Social Reconstruction Curriculum and Technology Education," *Journal of Technology Education*, 3 (2) (1992): 48-58.

7. See Burkhardt in this volume.

8. PISA, 2007.

9. See Keysar and Pasquale, Chapter 11.

10. A. D. Lutkus, M. A. Lauko, and D. M. Brockway, *The Nation's Report Card: Science 2005 Trial Urban District Assessment* (Washington, DC: National Center for Education Statistics, 2006), from http://nces.ed.gov/pubsearch/pubsinfo.asp?pubid=2007453 (accessed on December 23, 2007).

11. Current Population Survey (2007), Voting and Registration for the 2004 and 2006 General Elections (retrieved December 19, 2007 from BetaDataFerrett [computer program] available from www.thedataweb.org).

12. See Chapter 9.

13. D. H. Autor, L. F. Katz, and M. S. Kearney, *The Polarization of the U.S. Labor Market* (Cambridge, MA: National Bureau of Economic Research, 2006), from http://www.nber.org/papers/w11986.pdf (accessed on December 21, 2007).

14. Q. Schultze, "The Two Faces of Fundamentalist Higher Education," in *Fundamentalisms and Society: Reclaiming Sciences, the Family and Education* (Chicago, IL: University of Chicago Press, 1993), R. S. Appleby and M. E. Marty, eds.

15. See *Figure 10-2*.

16. U.S. National Science Board, 2003.

17. Ibid.

18. B. Groves, K. Markos, J. Reitmeyer, "Stem Cell Bond Issue Defeated; Voters also Say No to Sales Tax Question," *The Record* (Bergen, NJ), A01, November 7, 2007.

19. CNN.com Elections 2006, Missouri Amendment 2 Exit Poll, from http://www.cnn.com/ELECTION/2006//pages/results/states/MO/I/01/epolls.0.html (accessed on December 23, 2007).

20. CNN.com Election 2004, California Proposition 71 Exit Poll, from http://www.cnn.com/ELECTION/2004//pages/results/states/CA/I/02/epolls.0.html (accessed on December 23, 2007).

21. *Los Angeles Times* Exit Poll (2006), Institute of Governmental Studies, from http://www.latimes.com/media/acrobat/2006-11/26326083.pdf (accessed on December 17, 2007).

22. J. Knuckey, "A New Front in the Culture War?: Moral Traditionalism and Voting Behavior in U.S. House Elections," *American Politics Research*, 33 (5) (2005): 645-671;

Martin, 1996; C. Wilcox, *Onward Christian Soldiers?: The Religious Right in American Politics* (Boulder, CO: Westview Press, 1996).

23. K. Armstrong, *The Battle for God* (New York: Ballantine Books, 2001); E. Mendelsohn, "Religious Fundamentalism and the Sciences," in *Fundamentalisms and Society: Reclaiming Sciences, the Family and Education* (Chicago, IL: University of Chicago Press, 1993), R. S. Appleby and M. E. Marty, eds.

24. See Blackburn, Chapter 2.

25. C. Mooney, *The Republican War on Science* (New York: Basic Books, 2005).

26. See Chapter 9.

27. Initiative and Referendum Institute, Initiative Use (2006), from http://www.iandrinstitute.org/IRI%20Initiative%20Use%20(2006-11).pdf (accessed on November 27, 2007).

28. CNN.com Elections 2006, Missouri Amendment 2 Exit Poll.

29. M. P. Fiorina, "What Culture Wars?" *Wall Street Journal*, 2004 (A.14); M. J. Hetherington, "Resurgent Mass Partisanship: The Role of Elite Polarization," *American Political Science Review*, 95 (3) (2001): 619-631; N. M. McCarty, K.T. Poole, and H. Rosenthal, *Polarized America: The Dance of Ideology and Unequal Riches* (Cambridge, MA: MIT Press, 2006).

30. Poole and Rosenthal, "The Polarization of American Politics," *The Journal of Politics*, 46 (4) (1984): 1061-1079.

31. McCarty, Poole, and Rosenthal, 2006.

32. J. Navarro-Rivera, "The 'Wrong Kind': American Paranoids vs. Silent Revolution-aries in the 108th Congress," *Annual Meeting of the New England Political Science Association* (2007).

33. Mooney, 2005, 48.

34. Committee on Prospering in the Global Economy of the 21st Century, *Rising above the Gathering Storm: Energizing and Employing America for a Brighter Economic Future.* (Washington, DC: National Academies Press, 2007), 128.

35. See Keysar and Pasquale, Chapter 11.

36. D. L. Kleinman, "Democratizations of Science and Technology, " in D. L. Klein-man, ed., *Science, Technology, and Democracy* (Albany, NY: SUNY Press, 2000), 174.

37. A. de Tocqueville, *Democracy in America* (New York: Barnes & Noble, 2004).

38. R. Putnam, *Bowling Alone: The Collapse and Revival of American Community* (New York: Simon & Schuster, 2000); T. Skocpol, *Diminished Democracy: From Member-ship to Management in American Civic Life* (Norman, OK: University of Oklahoma Press, 2004).

39. D. C. Mutz, *Hearing the Other Side: Deliberative versus Participatory Democracy.* (Cambridge, UK: Cambridge University Press, 2006).

40. S. Eden, "Public Participation in Environmental Policy: Considering Scientific, Counter-scientific, and Non-scientific Contributions," *Public Understanding of Sci-ence,* 5 (1996): 183-204; T. Horlick-Jones, G. Rowe, and J. Walls, "Citizen Engage-ment Processes as Information Systems: The Role of Knowledge and the Concept of Translation Quality," *Public Understanding of Science,* 16 (2007): 259-278; R. Tytler, S. Duggan, and R. Gott, "Public Participation in an Environmental Dispute: Implications for Science Education," *Public Understanding of Science,* 10 (2001): 343-364.

41. Al Gore, *The Assault on Reason* (New York: Penguin Press, 2007).

42. M.C. Nisbet and C. Mooney, "Framing Science," *Science,* 316 (2007): 56.

43. Mooney, "Call for a Presidential Science Debate," *The Intersection,* from http://sci-enceblogs.com/intersection/2007/12/call_for_a_presidential_scienc.php (accessed on December 19, 2007).

44. Mooney, "Restoring the Office of Technology Assessment," *The Intersection.* from http://scienceblogs.com/intersection/2007/09/restoring_the_office_of_techno.php (accessed on December 19, 2007).

45. P. Z. Myers, "Bring back the OTA," *Pharyngula.* from http://scienceblogs.com/pharyngula/2007/09/bring_back_the_ota.php (accessed on December 19, 2007).

46. R. Millar, "Science Education for Democracy," in R. Levinson and J. Thomas, eds., *Science Today: Problem Or Crisis* (London: Routledge, 1997), 101.

47. Mooney, "Science + 1," from http://www.scienceprogress.org/2007/12/science_plus_one/ (accessed on December 21, 2007).

11. High School Students' Opinions about Science Education

Ariela Keysar & Frank L. Pasquale

Introduction

A solid grounding in science is widely considered to be crucial for the next generation of American adults. And providing science education to young children and adolescents is an overarching goal of educators nationwide. Yet studies show that although students are taking more science courses than in the past—at the prodding of teachers and guidance counselors—they are not absorbing much. The average science score at grade 12 on the National Assessment of Educational Progress test in 2005 was lower than in 1996, and showed no significant change from 2000.

In 2006, the average combined science literacy score for U.S. 15-year-old students was 489—slightly lower than the average (500) for 30 industrialized nations belonging to the Organization for Economic Cooperation and Development (OECD). As reported in detail by Kosmin and Navarro-Rivera in this volume,[1] U.S. students scored lower on science literacy than their peers in 16 of the other 29 OECD nations that participated in the Program for International Student Assessment (PISA).[2]

Beyond scientific literacy, PISA 2006 also looked at students' interest in, and attitudes toward, science. On the positive side, the vast majority of U.S. students say they value science—almost 90% said that "Science is important for helping us to understand the natural world." A large but slightly smaller majority of students also believes that science contributes to society: A little more than three-quarters said that "Advances in science and technology usually bring social benefits." On the personal level, though, support for science is somewhat thinner. Looking to the future, a little less than three-quarters said: "I

191

will use science in many ways when I am an adult." The majority shrinks further when it comes to students' enjoyment of learning science. Less than two-thirds of 15-year-old Americans reported that they enjoy learning science, saying that "I generally have fun when I am learning science topics." And less than half said that "I would like to work in a career involving science."

ISSSC High School Essay Contest

The theme of the curriculum development project of Trinity College's Institute for the Study of Secularism in Society and Culture (ISSSC) during the academic year 2006-07 was The Secular Tradition and Foundations of the Natural Sciences. The discussions among Trinity science professors and ISSSC staff raised concerns about science education in the U.S. The science professors drew attention to the need to improve science education at the high school level.

As valuable as the PISA survey is for assessing attitudes, a closed-ended questionnaire cannot explore in depth what students are thinking and why. To learn more, by integrating its two branches, teaching and research, ISSSC sponsored in early 2007 an essay contest open to students in all Connecticut high schools—public and private, including religious—whose question was: *Why do so many young Americans today show little interest in science education?*

The announcement about the essay contest was posted on the ISSSC website. In addition, letters were sent to all high schools in Connecticut asking science teachers to encourage their students to participate in the contest. The letters provided details about the rules of the contest and its prize.

The contest enabled young people, who are generally not heard from directly on issues of educational policy and practice, to offer insights into the frame of mind of their own generation. Unlike an opinion survey, the essay contest was not intended to gather a representative sample of students' feelings about science education, and we do not claim that the participants were representative of all Connecticut high school students.

The 81 participants in the essay contest were almost evenly distributed by gender, with 42 girls and 39 boys. Overall a dozen schools participated and the number of participating students from public schools exceeded only slightly those from private non-sectarian or religious schools. Students from 9th, 10th, and 11th grades as well as seniors submitted essays. They came from inner city, suburban and rural areas and various socioeconomic groups.

Those who participated were high-performing students. They were unusually enthusiastic about learning. Participants in an essay contest typically are students who feel comfortable expressing themselves in writing. They are more likely to be motivated by their teachers to take part in an assignment beyond their regular homework. Indeed many underscored a strong belief in the value of science education. Nonetheless, all of them accepted the premise of the contest, which is that many young Americans show little interest in science education.

The ideas expressed by the students highlight the issues of concern to high school students in the 21st century. We often hear and read reports about students from high school principals, teachers, counselors and parents. The essay contest is a rare occasion when students articulate their own views about the problems in the educational system and even suggest ways to solve them. In fact, in answering the question *Why do so many young Americans today show little interest in science education?* they did not mince words.

High School Students' Opinions

The following section quotes the students' own words, with their original grammar and spelling for the most part preserved intact. (Words and phrases used by the students are indicated in italics.)

The MTV Generation

A large number of high school students placed the blame on the general American culture and their own generation. They faulted the proliferation of technology that makes life easier yet more distracting, and they faulted themselves as well. This is, many argue, a generation that is all too ready to use available technology, or any other means, to avoid disciplined learning or sustained effort. Students describe their generation as *lazy, lacking in drive* or *persistence,* or motivated largely to find paths of least effort to fame, fortune, or financial security. For example:

> *Science requires a certain amount of diligence and perseverance, which is not found among the MTV generation. The youth have grown lazy and decadent, and refuse to put forth the amount of work necessary to excel in science. The alternatives presented by the mass media are far too tempting for the average youth. The sudden digitizing of entertainment has made Americans dependent on immediate and constant flow of enjoyable stimulus responses. . . . The current generation of students would much rather play video games and watch television than work for a solid future.*

> *Many people in my school are very lazy and don't want to work. They only care about the celebrities, popularity, and music.*

> *Young adults today are more interested in doing activities that require less work and more fun, in my opinion.*

In harsh words young people today are described as having *stopped thinking* and lacking curiosity about the world around them.

We haven't only given up thinking, but along with it curiosity.

This is also the *ADD generation*. Ubiquitous and fast-paced technological diversions are characterized as a conditioning *addiction*:

> *One of the most important things about science is that it takes time and careful observation. However, today all that Americans want to do is watch some mindless TV, and play videogames, with stimulus responses every 5-10 seconds. . . . The problem with this is that it creates a society with a very short attention span.*

Taking Science and Technology for Granted

Part of the problem, according to a number of essayists, lay with their peers for taking technology for granted. Dependent as they are on cell phones, computers, and iPods, young people aren't curious about how they work. As the students observed:

> *When one can connect to a virtual world with the flip of a switch, the incentive is lost to go out in the backyard and build rockets.*

> *Kids . . . are growing up surrounded with technology, from mechanized toys to video game consoles. . . . As a result of the great ease in which technology is found around us, it is a basic human reaction to just use those resources and not ponder much about it. . . Today's society thus assumes technology to just be there, uses it, and takes it for granted.*

Students observed that technology has made it ever easier to access information when and where it is needed. They think that technology puts

> *the answers to many scientific as well as other types of questions right at their fingertips and eliminating the desire for scientific education. Most would agree. . .why spend years of studying science when it's just a couple clicks of the mouse away?*

Science is Difficult

A recurring theme was the difficulty of science, which was described as *complicated, confusing* or *intimidating*. According to the essays, today's students expect everything to be *fun stuff*.

[S]cience can be very complicated. . . [and] not for the impatient of heart. Most science takes a lot of patience to grasp the theories and intricate details. . . . To some it can be very confusing. Science also takes a lot of effort to reach conclusions. Learning science can be fairly intimidating to people.

. . .[T]he sciences and technologies that surround our lives today may be confusing and intimidating. . . . Many people may be pushed away from [them] *because the explanations of how things work may confuse. . . or intimidate them to a point where they are no longer interested or curious.*

Criticizing Teaching Methods

Many of the high school students also criticized the way science is taught. They don't like being lectured to and prefer the *fun part* of science, emphasizing their desire for more learning by doing.

[Y]oung Americans have the right to hate science education. It is a subject that has no personality if it's not taught right. Science can be confusing, hard to follow, and very time consuming.

Science itself is interesting, but the way it is taught is usually not. . .[S]chools are what I like to kindly call "diabolical memorization emporiums."

[C]hildren are turned off by teaching methods commonly found in schools today [like] lists, facts, and figures. . . . [W]hen a teacher sits at the front of a classroom and rambles on about boring facts and figures every hour of the school day, they will not get through to students!

The students suggest that there is inadequate emphasis on hands-on, laboratory, and experimental activity that better engage students and bring the sciences alive.

If there were fewer lectures and more hands-on experimentation and research where students were. . .interactively involved, there would be an increase in science. . .among students.

Some students suggest that problems with science education reflect larger social and academic priorities in American society that give it short shrift and inadequate resources (such as laboratories and experimental equipment). Others assert that education, in general, is poorly valued in American culture. A number of students point to specific issues, such as a tendency to *teach to tests* or stress quantity (of information crammed or regurgitated) rather than quality (of educational engagement and experience). Several blame the "No Child Left

Behind" initiative for a myopic focus on testing and the basics (reading, writing, mathematics), and for reduced emphasis on science and the arts. To this point, the title of one essay was *"Every Child Left Behind: A Critique of the Science Education System in America."* That student concluded: *"young Americans are not interested in science because of the faulty education system."*

A few students even suggest that too many teachers are poorly prepared to teach science, which requires considerable knowledge and distinctive (hands-on) teaching methods. According to these students, the intrinsic difficulty of the subject matter, coupled with *tedious* or *boring* pedagogy, leads many students to fear science classes and to avoid them as much as possible. Among all school subjects, science and math are widely viewed as the greatest threats to grade-point averages, peer social standing, and self-esteem.

Low Return on the Investment

Students attributed the lack of interest in science to the belief that careers in science are relatively low-paying. One asked a fundamental question: *"What do you do with a science degree?"*

Students who are thinking about career paths express concern that there will be little or no incentive or payoff for substantial investments of time, effort, or financial commitment in science education. Beyond the immediate drawback of lost social status among fellow students, scientific careers seem to many to offer an unattractive investment-reward ratio. Students believe that there are less demanding, less education-intensive, more exciting and more lucrative alternatives to science careers. For example:

> *Science and technology might be a fun and exciting choice as a career, but it can be extremely difficult to master all the skills required. . . . [Those] who qualify to be scientists and engineers lack the desire for it because of insufficient salary. . . . [S]cientists sit and work tirelessly in a cubicle around the clock with almost no free time. Not only that, the high end of science is still underpaid compared to other careers. . . . Why would people choose a job that is tiring, requires a great amount of skill and focus, and causes stress for little money? The only other reason why people would choose such a disadvantageous job besides devoted passion is fame, but science does not give people fame either.*

> *There is a wide variety of career choices in science, from medicine to environment protection. Careers in science require a great deal of schooling and are often underpaid. I believe that the younger generations . . . want to have it all, the nice car, the big house. . . . Careers in science can be very*

*rewarding, and give a great deal back to the community, but take so much.
. .[and] are underpaid. The . . . younger generations just aren't willing to
give.*

*I think that science has one major problem and this is. . . what do you do
with a science degree? . . . There aren't too many people in this world getting
rich off the science industry.*

*A job such as a chemist wouldn't exactly fit into the luxurious lifestyle that
many people have in mind.*

*Although careers in science are more lucrative than they were at the turn
of the century, in comparison to the dream jobs of American teens, they are
greatly out shadowed. Therefore, if a career as a researcher isn't as lucrative
as that of a stock broker, then without intrinsic motivation there is little
incentive for an American child to pursue such a career.*

*[S]cience. . .requires skill, determination, intelligence and devotion....It
requires lots of hard work. . . . Many people don't want to put that much
into a career; they want a cushy job.*

Some suggest that students have concluded, extrapolating from news
about corporations shifting jobs abroad, that scientific and engineering jobs are
dwindling in the United States.

*Receiving a broad education in technology can...seem unappealing because
many technology jobs have been outsourced to countries like India and
China. The people who had these jobs in the United States are now losing
them. As a student . . . it is a wise decision to pick a field of study that can
be used in their jobs after they graduate. If jobs that utilize technology are
being outsourced, then what is the point of receiving an education in it if
there are no jobs . . .?*

*Another reason why most people aren't interested in studying the sciences
is because they are constantly hearing how jobs are being shifted to other
countries. . . . Thus, people hear from other people that it's a bad idea to go
into something in the science and technology area because they would have
a hard time finding a job.*

In a handful of essays, it is suggested that many students feel the need for
science has declined, the truly significant advances in science and technology
have already been made, and that it will therefore be difficult to produce new
findings or develop new patents:

Science. . .has essentially passed its hay [sic] *day.*

As for science, it's the same old thing just put in different ways [or] terms. don't really "need" science.

The hole scientists keep digging for themselves is [that] it's hard to top the technology advancements we've created over the past quarter century.

[I]t becomes harder and harder for scientists and engineers to devise something that somebody else has not already patented.

Many indicated that students today simply see little practical relevance in the study of science. Particularly among those who have no interest in scientific careers, utility or application in their everyday or future lives seems limited. They wish only to *make it through* science classes and graduate, *"hoping that they won't have to learn science ever again."*

Religion and Science

Religion was not generally cited by these students as a deterrent to scientific understanding or pursuit. One suggested that alternative ways of thinking, philosophical and religious, are supplanting scientific worldviews. A resurgence of religion *"leads to a decrease in the amount of people taking and earning degrees in science."* But another student observed:

Many people believe that the conflict between science and religion is increasing. . . . People believe that you have to be an atheist to accept science. I believe you can be religious and scientific.

In one notable essay, rather than conflict, an intensely rewarding fusion of scientific inquiry and religious belief was described:

[S]cience is what adds beauty to our universe and makes everything so much more amazing. . . . Personally, I find the view science gives us of the universe as intriguing as I do because I love my God, the creator of this universe, and with each new thing I learn, some of God's glory is revealed to me. . . .

Although I could never completely understand how every single aspect works together, I am now somewhat familiar with the intense complexity of all things and therefore I am also reminded of our glorious creator and wanting to learn more. Although this reason alone is more than enough to keep me interested in science, I also realize that there are many individuals just as enthralled about the subject who don't share my faith.

This is one of a handful of students who reported active engagement in scientific pursuits. Their experiences are particularly instructive regarding antidotes to many of the negative perceptions summarized here.

Blaming the Media

Finally, the mass media came in for blame for not providing an appealing image of science and portraying scientists as boring *geeks*.

> *Hollywood has portrayed many nerds as lovers of science. That's probably one of the reasons that students don't openly show an interest in science or show any interest at all. Students are probably afraid that they will be made fun of and outcast. . . . Science to them is for nerds and nerds only. There is nothing cool about the earth and all of its organisms. Unless this stereotype can be erased then this trend will probably continue.*

> *Kids might not have even taken a science class yet but they will still put a label on it as boring and stupid. The people to blame for this outlook on science are the makers of movies, TV shows, commercials, and the media. [In] "Saved by the Bell" [television show] . . . people that were good in science and got good grades were the 'geeks.' If you put on any movie nowadays, there is a 65% chance one of the characters is a nerd or a mad scientist.*

> *When most people think of a scientist, they think of a man in a white lab coat with hair that is sticking out with electricity going through it holding a beaker that contains a crazy concoction in it. This isn't exactly appealing. . . .*

The media are implicated in another way. By comparison with an insistent drum-beat of fame and celebrity, the world and work of science are notably unattractive. In America, *"we are. . .absorbed with celebrities,"* athletes, and entertainers. As one student wrote:

> *Another thing about science is that there is little appeal about it. From my point of view, becoming a scientist or a chemist or whatever is not that appealing at all. When most people are asked of there [sic] dreams I would put money on it that one out of a hundred say that [they] want to be a famous scientist, it usually falls under the line of being a famous athlete or movie/ music star, not having anything to do with science at all.*

Medicine—that is, being a physician rather than medical research—is presented as the quintessential scientific career by several students. *"When people think of science, they tend to tie medicine into the picture."* Again, based on general impression and media portrayals, many conclude that careers in medicine, and so science in general, are inordinately demanding:

> *Once you have a science occupation . . .your spare moments for quality time with your family and friends are lost. The show "House". . . demonstrates the strenuous commitment that someone will take on while employed in a scientific job, showing the basic tasks and obligations that someone choosing to be a doctor will encounter. . . .[I]n this line of work your job comes before anything else.*

In non-medical portrayals, scientific careers are often rendered as *tedious* work performed by *"a nerdy guy working in a white lab coat in a basement." "The stereotype of a scientist has scared many students away from attempting a career in science."*

Hopeful Signs

All is not hopeless. It should be borne in mind that these Connecticut students were asked for critical diagnoses of science education's ills rather than prognoses, cures, or even a balanced picture of the education system. Even so, amid the gloomy diagnoses there are glimmers of hope. In their words:

> *Science is very important in understanding the world. The better educated, the more* [one] *can understand in the field of science, and the more he will know about himself and the world he lives in. All that one is* [and] *what one does . . . are aspects of science. Not only is it good to understand this world, it is important to improve it. . . . Society is based on what is known about science in the world. When society is improved, it benefits everyone. Science is also significant to everyone's life because it cures diseases. . . . Science is a subject that is great to have an interest in because it leads to a great . . . opportunity to change the world for the betterment of humankind.*

Conclusion

The high school students who participated in the Institute for the Study of Secularism in Society and Culture (ISSSC) essay contest assert that for a host of reasons the sciences are unappealing as courses of study or as career options. In their view, science is highly stereotyped, little understood, and generally poorly taught. It is widely viewed as intimidating and impenetrably complex. Moreover, they describe young Americans as lazy and not curious. Their lack of interest prevents young people today from "genuinely experiencing the world" around them and diminishes the possibilities for American society as a whole to compete in science and technology globally.

Clearly, these Connecticut high school students do not represent all high school students. Naturally, the students who submitted essays are neither high school drop-outs, nor average students. They represent more elite students, and are quite different from the adult non-voters described by Kosmin and Navarro-Rivera in this volume.[3] It is hard to predict the views and opinions of the majority of Connecticut high school students who did not submit an essay. Possibly, but very unlikely, the non-participating students have more positive perceptions and some may even disagree with the claim that young Americans today show little interest in science education. Alternatively, some of those who did not respond to our call for papers might have exhibited even darker, more negative views and sentiments toward science.

One may think of the student essayists quoted above not as research subjects but as young social scientists, offering their own observations and insights into the intellectual milieu in Connecticut high schools today. Seen in this light, their suggestions are worth taking seriously because of the acuteness of their analysis of current perceptions of science education, even if the essayists themselves happen to be high-performing outliers.

Although their analysis seems bleak, there is good news between the lines, since many of the problems the students cite are fixable. The idea that scientists are poorly paid, for example, is simply a misperception that can be corrected with better information (see below). Science education, currently a turnoff, can be improved as well.

Education is a lengthy process and we cannot expect to transform instantly the values cherished in a culture. Nevertheless, we propose some ideas to win the hearts of high school students and convince them "to give science a chance."

First, inform students that science can be a lucrative career as well as a satisfying one. Contrary to the Connecticut students' perceptions, in a capitalistic society the American dream "to be rich" could be accomplished by those pursuing science as a career. The May 2006 National Occupational Employment and Wage Estimates collected by the Bureau of Labor Statistics of the U.S. Department of Labor reveal that there are many lucrative options for scientists in the U.S., helping them to achieve the American dream with earnings more than twice the national average (see *Figure 11-1*).

Figure 11-1

Salary Statistics for a Range of Science-Based Occupations, 2006[4]

Selected Occupation	Mean Annual Wage
Petroleum Engineers	$101,620
Computer and Information Scientists, Research	$ 96,440
Physicists	$ 95,580
Computer Hardware Engineers	$ 91,280
Aerospace Engineers	$ 89,260
Computer Software Engineers, System Software	$ 87,250
Biochemists and Biophysicists	$ 80,900
All U. S. occupations	$ 39,190

These high annual wages of scientists are not surprising given the chances to make money in a modern and highly advanced economy, such as in biotechnology, pharmaceuticals, and information technology. Opportunities to innovate remain plentiful.

Second, teachers should publicize the accomplishments of today's scientists, from curing diseases to inventing software. Americans are by far the leading recipients of Nobel Prizes, the most celebrated and highly recognized prize for science and scientists worldwide. Not unimportantly to students' financial aspirations, the Nobel Prize carries a generous amount of money with it. In the same vein, it is worth making students aware that scientists are highly admired by adult Americans. According to The Harris Poll from 2006, as reported by Beit-Hallahmi[5] in this volume, the American public ranks scientist as a prestigious occupation below only firefighter, doctor and nurse, and above teacher, military officer, police officer and priest/minister/clergyman. Beit-Hallahmi speculates that being a "scientist is rated close to those occupations that regularly strive to save lives, regardless of risk and effort."

Third, one important message we learn both from the high school students as well as from a science teacher, William Cobern,[6] in this volume, is that better methods of teaching are crucial in winning the hearts of students. The pedagogy that Cobern is advocating, which is similar to what the students are asking for, involves "teaching of science by inquiry." The high school students were very articulate in expressing their wishes to explore science by having more "hands-on" and laboratory experiments. Therefore, state and local boards of education and science teachers ought to consider some of the rules suggested by Cobern when they design science curricula in order to accommodate young people's preference for scientific explorations.

Standardized testing is one culprit in the decline of hands-on experimentation in science classes—and thus the declining interest of students in science. After all, teachers can communicate more facts and garner higher test scores for their students by teaching from the textbook than by supervising in-class experimentation. This is unfortunate because students who learn by doing achieve a much deeper and longer-lasting understanding of the subject matter than those who study from textbooks and class notes. This is a difficult problem to solve since standardized testing is deeply ingrained in the educational system. Perhaps innovative educators could build laboratory methods into future standardized tests by devising an experiment that students could perform as part of the test.

Advancing and improving U.S. science education so it can compete in the global market will require raising the bar by applying nationwide the suggestion of one Connecticut high school student:

> *I also believe that our Country is missing the bigger picture. Rather than trying to compete with other nations, or focusing on advancing our knowledge in math and science, our country is far too focused on competing with the neighboring town, the other community, or the other state. Our boards of education are focused more on test scores and statistics—rather than on the more profound task of challenging young American minds to aim higher.*

Endnotes

1. See Chapter 10.

2. Programme for International Student Assessment. *PISA 2006: Science Competencies for Tomorrow's World.* Paris: OECD. from http://www.sourceoecd.org/upload/980701 1e1.pdf, accessed on December 4, 2007 (2007).

3. See Chapter 10.

4. Source: U.S. Department of Labor, Bureau of Labor Statistics.

5. See Chapter 7.

6. See Chapter 5.

INDEX

Contributors

Dr. Juan Antonio Aguilera Mochón is Professor of Biochemistry and Molecular Biology and in the Instituto de la Paz y los Conflictos (Peace and Conflict Institute) at the University of Granada, Spain. He is a board member of Granada Laica and Europa Laica (Secular Granada; Secular Europe).

Dr. Benjamin Beit-Hallahmi is Professor of Psychology at the University of Haifa, Israel. He is the author, co-author, editor, or co-editor of 17 books and monographs on the psychology of religion, social identity, and personality development. Among his best-known publications are *The Psychology of Religious Behaviour, Belief and Experience, The Psychoanalytic Study of Religion,* and *Psychoanalysis, Identity, and Ideology.* In 1993, he was the recipient of the William James Award (Division 36 of the American Psychological Association) for his contributions to the psychology of religion.

Dr. Daniel G. Blackburn is the Thomas S. Johnson Distinguished Professor of Biology at Trinity College, Hartford. A graduate of the University of Pittsburgh, he earned his M.Sc. and Ph.D. at Cornell University. He joined the Trinity faculty in 1988 and has served as chair of the Biology Department since 2002. Blackburn teaches courses in zoology, electron microscopy, and evolution, and his research focus is on function and evolution of reproductive specializations in reptiles.

Dr. Jeffrey Burkhardt is Professor of Ethics and Policy Studies in the Institute of Food and Agricultural Sciences of the University of Florida. For the past 20 years, he has worked in a science and technology-development organization devoted to food and natural resource problem-solving. He teaches courses on agriculture and natural resource ethics, science ethics, and the philosophy of economics. His research has focused on the human and environmental impacts of agricultural biotechnology, which some regard as the technological fix for issues associated with population growth and global sustainability. Dr. Burkhardt chaired the Council on Agricultural Science and Technology Task Force on Agricultural Ethics, which issued the report, *Agricultural Ethics,* in 2005.

Dr. William Cobern is Professor of Biological Sciences and Science Education and Director of the Mallinson Institute for Science Education at Western Michigan University. He began his science education career as a high school biology and chemistry teacher, and has also taught science at the elementary and college levels. At the Institute, he teaches a variety of courses for science teacher development and science education research. He has an active research program funded by the National Science Foundation. In 2006, Dr. Cobern was elected a Fellow of the American Association for the Advancement of Science.

Dr. Austin Dacey is contributing editor with *Skeptical Inquirer* magazine and a representative to the United Nations for the Center for Inquiry, a think tank advancing the secular, scientific outlook in public affairs. A philosopher by training, he writes and lectures widely on the intersection of science, religion, and ethics. He is author of the new book, *The Secular Conscience.*

Dr. David E. Henderson is Professor of Chemistry at Trinity College, Hartford. He obtained his Ph.D. at the University of Massachusetts Amherst in analytical chemistry in 1975 and joined the faculty of Trinity College in 1977. His scholarly publications involve spectroscopy chromatography and mass spectrometry of antioxidants, metals, peptides, fats, acid rain, and mummies. He has directed the Interdisciplinary Science Program at Trinity and the Environmental Science Program and has been Chair of the Chemistry Department. He has authored three Reacting courses; *Evolution in Kansas 1999, Acid in the European Environment-1979-89*, and *The Council of Nicaea* -326 CE.

Dr. Ariela Keysar is Associate Research Professor of Public Policy and Law and the Associate Director of the Institute for the Study of Secularism in Society and Culture (ISSSC) at Trinity College, Hartford. She is the co-editor of *Secularism & Secularity: Contemporary International Perspectives* and co-author of *Religion in a Free Market.* A demographer, Dr. Keysar has conducted national surveys on fertility and family formation. Most recently, she is one of the principal investigators of an international study of worldviews and opinions of scientists, a series of web surveys conducted by ISSSC.

Dr. Barry A. Kosmin is the Founding Director of the Institute for the Study of Secularism in Society and Culture and Research Professor, Public Policy and Law Program at Trinity College, Hartford. A sociologist, Dr. Kosmin has been principal investigator of many large national social surveys and opinion polls in Europe, Africa, Asia, and the U.S., including the CUNY 1990 National Survey of Religious Identification and the American Religious Identification Survey 2001. He is co-author of *One Nation under God: Religion in Contemporary American Society, Religion in a Free Market*, and co-editor of *Secularism & Secularity.*

Dr. Jon D. Miller is the John A. Hannah Professor of Integrative Studies at Michigan State University. He has measured the public understanding of science and technology in the United States for the last three decades and has pioneered the definition and measurement of scientific literacy. His approach to the public understanding of science has been replicated in more than 40 countries. Dr. Miller is the Director of the Longitudinal Study of American Youth (LSAY). He is a Fellow of the American Association for the Advancement of Science and recently completed his second six-year term on the AAAS Committee on the Public Understanding of Science and Technology.

Juhem Navarro-Rivera is a Research Fellow at the Institute for the Study of Secularism in Society and Culture (ISSSC). He holds a B.A. from the University of Puerto Rico and is a Ph.D. candidate in political science at the University of Connecticut. His interest is in the politics of health and drug issues, and his current research deals with political representation and opposition to evidence-based HIV/AIDS prevention policy.

Dr. Frank L. Pasquale is a Research Associate at ISSSC. He received his doctorate in cultural anthropology at Northwestern University. Following this, he was a Research Fellow at the East-West Center in Hawaii, where he studied Chinese, Japanese, and American cultures and communication styles. He is currently engaged in research on forms of secularity in the United States, and he has written and lectured widely on this and related topics. His most recent publications include an overview of empirical study of "unbelief and irreligion" in *The New Encyclopedia of Unbelief* and a report on "The 'nonreligious' in the Pacific Northwest" in *Secularism & Secularity*.

Dr. Robert T. Pennock is Professor of Philosophy of Science at Michigan State University in Lyman Briggs College, the Departments of Philosophy, Computer Science and Engineering, and the Ecology, Evolutionary Biology and Behavior program. The author of *Tower of Babel: the Evidence against the New Creationism,* he was called as an expert witness in the 2005 *Kitzmiller* case which ruled that including Intelligent Design creationism in a public school is unconstitutional. Dr. Pennock is a Fellow of the American Association for the Advancement of Science. He serves on the AAAS Committee on the Public Understanding of Science and Technology and also on the National Academies of Science authoring committee for the NAS book *Science, Evolution and Creationism.*

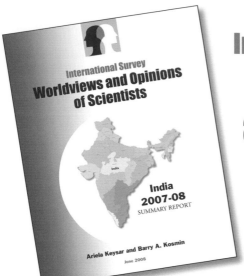

International Survey
Worldviews and Opinions of Scientists

India 2007-08

SUMMARY REPORT

Ariela Keysar and Barry A. Kosmin

June 2008

The report may be downloaded free of charge at www.trincoll.edu/secularisminstitute

This is a summary report containing highlights of an international, academic web survey, Worldviews and Opinions of Scientists in India, conducted by the Institute for the Study of Secularism and Culture (ISSSC) of Trinity College in Hartford, Conn. It covers a demographic profile of Indian scientists; their opinions on political, economic, and scientific issues; and their worldviews and beliefs about contemporary moral and ethical issues.

The survey was conducted in cooperation with the Center for Inquiry India between August 2007 and January 2008. The large national sample of Indian scientists, the first of its kind, included 1,100 participants from 130 universities and research institutes.

Secularism & Secularity
Contemporary International Perspectives

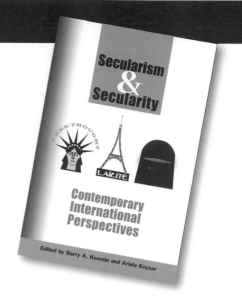

AUSTRALIA • CANADA • DENMARK • FRANCE
GREAT BRITAIN • INDIA • IRAN • ISRAEL • UNITED STATES

Edited by Barry A. Kosmin and Ariela Keysar

ISBN: 978-0-9794816-0-4

**Individual chapters may be downloaded free of charge at
www.trincoll.edu/secularisminstitute**

The timing has never been better for a volume of essays by international scholars about Secularism & Secularity. Despite all appearances and claims to the contrary, the number of people with a secular outlook is growing swiftly, not only in the U.S. but in such countries as Australia, Canada, and France. At the same time, secularism as a political philosophy is playing a pivotal role in debates over national identity in Israel, India, and Denmark.

The editors' goal is to study secularism "not as the mirror image of religion, but as an intellectual and social force in its own right." In exploring the varieties of secular experience around the world, the reader finds that the seemingly well-defined terms of "secularism" and "secularity" are actually highly context-specific and freighted with political significance. This is an important and fascinating collection of essays for a volatile era.

This book may be ordered for $10.00, shipping included.
Send check and mailing information to: **ISSSC**
                                                Trinity College
                                                300 Summit Street
Or call 860-297-2381   **Hartford, CT 06106-3100**